WITHDRAWN

The concrete architecture of Riccardo Morandi

Giorgio Boaga/Benito Boni

The concrete architecture of

Riccardo Morandi

introduction by Riccardo Morandi

PRAEGER / NEW YORK / WASHINGTON

BOOKS THAT MATTER

Published in the United States of America in 1966
by Frederick A. Praeger, Inc. Publishers
111, Fourth Avenue, New York 3, N.Y.
Library of Congress Catalog Card Number: 66-11378

ORIGINAL ITALIAN EDITION (C) 1962 EDIZIONI DI COMUNITA, MILAN
NEW ENLARGED EDITION, TRANSLATED INTO ENGLISH (C) 1965 ALEC TIRANTI LTD. LONDON
PRINTED BY MATRO LTD. LONDON/BOUND BY MANSELL & CO LTD. LONDON
Made and printed in the United Kingdom

CONTENTS

A2

When the 'Science of Construction' (as we generally describe the study of the stability of deformable bodies in relation to the forces acting upon them)—from the earliest intuitions of Leonardo da Vinci, the discoveries of Galileo, Robert Hooke's statement *sic tensio ut vis* and the enunciation of the elastic theory by Navier and Cauchy—started its rapid development during the last century, side by side with the development of the technology of materials came the development of modern civil engineering.

At the same time the modern engineer appeared on the scene—serious-minded, determined to accept nothing that was not based on strict reasoning and precise scientific results—who, as soon as the appropriate materials became available to him, produced works of outstanding value, which are acclaimed today as masterpieces of architecture.

A new idea, allied to a new or improved material, has always found a designer of strong personality capable of grasping and exploiting its potentialities (*les intuitions heureuses des pioniers* as Colonetti put it). Only later came the men of more mediocre quality, and various obstacles and difficulties arose—which were themselves useful in restraining a sometimes excessive enthusiasm.

In 1884 Eiffel built his viaduct over the Trujère at Garabit with a central arch spanning 607 ft. and in 1885 Fowler and Baker built the Forth Bridge ; both after the production of cast and drawn steel had started in 1882. This latter bridge, with three spans of over 1,700 ft. is, in my opinion, one of the finest and most important works of our time and I hope that it will endure long enough to show our most distant descendants one of the great monuments of our civilization.

In 1904 Hennebique designed the admirable Risorgimento Bridge in Rome. This was in the earliest days of reinforced concrete, using artificial Portland cement which at that time had only been in commercial production a few years and had a strength of about one-seventh of that of today.

In 1927 Freyssinet built his beautiful bridges over the Marne, with spans of 230 ft., when pre-stressing was little more than an ideal, grasped by him and by few others.

And alongside these great works (I have only mentioned a few, though perhaps the most important) a group of great intellectuals with scientific knowledge have created a wonderful study based on thought and experience—the Science of Construction—evolved almost entirely in the last century and the early years of the present one.

During this period scientists and engineers lived and developed together in complete symbiosis, with, however, the vague hope on the part of the former of being able to replace the latter by well-drawn-up formulae, manuals and tables, or at least of reducing them to the role of mere arithmeticians.

At the same time the architects were at work, quite separate, and given over for the most part to the study for reproduction purposes, of ancient forms of style and construction; they were guardians of a tradition which was only being rejuvenated by ever more false and decadent decoration. If, in a few instances (a railway station, a city arcade, an auditorium) it became necessary for the architect and the specialist in the new type of structure to be associated, the former carefully covered up the work of the latter, or 'decorated' it (always with the aim of reducing its impact), possibly with flowers and leaves.

Only the so-called (and rather despised) 'industrial structures' could be entrusted to the technologists alone, and they in designing them considered only the judgement of the theoretical scientists—which was based solely on whether their formulae were precisely applied. In these structures all considerations other than those of function and economy were taboo; a factory building was a great barrack, squalid and supremely inexpressive.

The few exceptions (Behrens in Germany in the first years of the century, and, soon after, Gropius, one of the great pioneers) gave first signs of the new times.

In the '20s, while we were still young students, we watched the outbreak of the architectural revolution, essentially the outcome of the rationalist movement, and we found it fascinating. The potentialities of modern structure were revealed, particularly those of reinforced concrete; as is well known, the release from previous repressive systems of walling, large spans, cantilevers, the interaction of the different structural elements, are all characteristics of a development which eventually came near to stylistic expression.

In a very few years came the disappearance of the walls concealing the reinforced concrete structure which was thus revealed in all its starkness, with all its possibilities, and ready to play the leading part in one of the great periods of the art of construction.

The spread of reinforced concrete brought with it the creation of a large group of so-called 'calculators', working in close collaboration with the architects, who by now had become imbued with a fresh vitality and reaching out towards a far wider range of training and interests—the outcome, in Italy, of the founding of a College (later a University Faculty) of Architecture.

From this time on there began, together with collaboration (often fruitless because lacking in conviction), the controversy between engineers and architects; the former with all their prejudices their contempt for the irrational, and their lack of interest, the latter strong in their new-found faith. And so came about the phenomenon of two types of men condemned to work together in an atmosphere of mutual incomprehension, and, it must be recognized, with a tendency to conceal, or at least to reduce to insignificance, the contribution of the engineer; resulting in an even greater doubt on his part as to the aesthetic result of the joint effort.

However, soon after the revelation of the fundamental architectural values of the structure, some doubts arose as to the validity of some of the boundaries between architecture and engineering, and with the beginning of the controversy—even today far from being resolved—even the most talented engineers took up opposing positions.

Those with the more scientific training ignored the new developments, shut themselves up in an ever more hermetic intransigeance, and gave themselves increasingly to a worship of calculation as such, as if it were an absolute truth to which everything else should be subordinated. And the architects were very ready to accuse them of aesthetic insensibility and of small interest in the immense material and spiritual needs of mankind.

Even today there are some who ask for structures to be designed solely on strictly rational—even scientific—methods. Engineers, in fact, who have the mentality of pure mathematicians and theoretical physicists—that is to say of those whose function is to extend knowledge of physical truths and to provide the technicians with fresh bases for their application.

In fact, we are living in a period when fundamental concepts are continually being revised. For the traditional 'elastic theory', previously used, we are substituting ultimate load design, and perhaps one day we shall substitute for this something else—more deeply thought out and perhaps simpler —when, as the physicists are leading us to hope, a conjunction between a simplified theory of the molecular structure of materials and a clarified and more deeply worked out description of the phenomena shall have taken place.

And in these conditions can the engineer be uncompromising about his calculations, or should he consider them merely as the best tool available to him at the moment?

Some, especially in the past, have reacted with the usual argument of 'ignorance' to the critics' recognition that they have achieved outstanding feats of stylistic expression.

Freyssinet, to whom someone wrote that the famous Orly hangers (1921) were one of the most important works of modern architecture, replied:

> 'After much research and hesitation, I decided to combine certain shapes which could be constructed economically. I looked for nothing more, and not for one moment did I think of the artistic effect.'

Clearly his great engineer's heart had thought for him!

Others finally, affirm, and make this the basis of their works, that every structure which is *right* structurally will automatically be right aesthetically. The architect objects that this is not true, accuses the engineer of aesthetic insensibility and rightly senses the weakness of the argument.

In fact, every solution, by the fact that it is structurally correct, may aspire to its own aesthetic validity, but only if it has also been studied from this point of view, and has been carefully chosen from among the many structurally correct possibilities.

It is, in fact, only necessary to be moderately familiar with the design of structures to realize that it is always possible, within certain limits, to solve a problem—functionally, structurally and economically—in several equally valid ways.

At this point the final choice of solution among the numerous possible ones, and the loving care given to the formal details (quite independently of the requirements of calculation) transcend the purely technical aspect and, intentionally or not, contribute to artistic creation.

This is a well known fact, and already over forty years ago Robert Maillart, the great structural designer, said:

> 'The opinion is prevalent that calculations alone should determine dimensions. However, in view of the impossibility of assessing every influence, calculations can only be a basis for the constructor, who must take all these influences into account.
>
> 'According to circumstances, the results of calculation may be applied directly, or may undergo a change. And this second alternative always arises when a constructor, and not a mathematician, is at work.

10

And Piccinato, one of the most enlightened architects of my generation, adds :

'Let the designer be capable of expressing himself in human terms, outstripping, in this method of expression, those technical aids which science places at his disposal and which can only be one instrument among many.'

*   *   *

In the early 'thirties, after completing my Civil Engineering studies in Rome—completed in a strange academic atmosphere still overshadowed by the precepts of Vignola with structures timidly hidden away among them—and after a few years' apprenticeship in Southern Italy, I started up in Rome in the liberal profession of a 'calculator' of reinforced concrete frames for dwellings. A long, patient preparation in order to fulfil as well as possible the function of a specialist technician in the solution of structural problems.

After a few years I developed a great interest in the new technique of prestressing. Continually seeking for increased scope for its application, I flatter myself that even I played a part in the logical development of the process of thought which led from reinforced concrete to prestressed concrete.

From the idea of taking up in steel reinforcement the tensile stresses existing in a concrete structure, to that of using the steel to produce compressive stresses to counterbalance the tensile stresses, is but a short step. All that was required was to place the structure in a state of co-action by means of a suitable prestressing technique.

And so I began to get ready, and to await the moment—still more than fifteen years away—when prestressing would enable me, and many others, to produce solutions surpassing our highest hopes during those far away years of dreams, of study, and of development.

When, gradually, the time came to design by the application of external forces more and more interesting works—large industrial buildings, auditoria, sports stadia and bridges—the time came, too, to apply—coherently, for life—that in which I have always believed : in short, Maillart's words.

And I applied all my energies to studying the functional characteristics of each work, going into its minutest details ; to the cost aspect, not only in terms of money but in terms of the expenditure of mental and physical energy by those responsible for it, and their personal risk ; to its adherence to the train of thought which guides one at a particular time ; also to the spiritual point of view ; finally, to its structural aspects. Here the tendency of the last few years to seek out complicated and often absurd forms, the delight of formalists and of lovers of complex expression, is something I have always successfully avoided, even at the cost of being considered rather old fashioned and somewhat lacking in the mathematical point of view (which, in fact, I think I am).

I have always liked simple, easily controllable projects (remembering, too, the possibility of imperfect workmanship) in which the arrangement and form of the different components clearly expresses their static function—that is, in the last analysis, their reason for existence. And, from the point of view of discipline, in adopting a certain solution I have always let myself be guided by the requirements of function, economics and statics. But at this point the final solution has been chosen after conscientious research into detail, deepened as time went on by all the similar problems which I have had to solve.

Let me, for example, quote my long search to express through its visible structure the essential nature of a large cinema—from the Giulio Cesare cinema in Rome (1934) to the Maestoso, also in Rome (1957). Or the research into a large arch bridge, from the San Niccolò Bridge in Florence (1946) to the Fiumarella Bridge (1960). Lastly, the formal research on bridges supported by inclined tension members, either above (the Maracaibo Bridge or the Polcevera viaduct, Genoa) or below (via Olimpica, Rome, or the bridge over the Vela at Sulmona). It is a branch of research which I hope I shall be able to pursue for a long time to come.

Altogether life has not been easy—always involved in controversy, either with engineers with a more conservative and academic outlook than mine, or with architects—particularly those with prejudices on questions of style. A life lived in the midst of suspicion on the part of society with its changing currents of opinion. A difficult life, which perhaps has been responsible for a certain asperity in myself and in my work.

We have, in short, tried to carry out a work of synthesis and clarification, and to create a basis for a better collaboration between two opposing types of mentality. What have we achieved? Not much, to judge by some of the latest developments.

Too many engineers still boast of their lack of interest in formal values and, here and there, among architects, one sees either the search for complicated form, or a return to already outmoded designs, with a consequent denial of structural values, relegating these purely to the realm of statics. And they quote the example of Le Corbusier, with his church of Ronchamp, as described by Henry-Russell Hitchcock at the recent U.I.A. Congress in London.

However, we are now resigned to ending our days without comfort, between two opposing groups and between two fires.

It is, nonetheless, sufficient to be recognized as always true to ourselves, and fundamentally incapable of the enormous reversals of opinion which we have seen take place in a few years, from the most uncompromising, indeed, inflamed, structuralism, to the 'neo-Liberty' style, from an exaltation of the values of reinforced concrete, to their denial and, in its place, a passionate affection for steel structure, even though this is treated on the formal basis of Vignola's famous precepts.

As for me, I go quietly on with my work, alert to every suggestion arising from the developing study of statics, from the advent of new materials and, above all, from my ordinary human desire to renew myself in the development of living conditions. All this, moreover, without deflection from my fundamental concepts and without any change of belief. I hope that young people will recognize in the more significant aspects of my work, shown here, a proof of this 'quest for coherence'.

Boaga and Boni, two young architects, who have gone through my records most intelligently to make my work clear, have judged it in this way. I thank them sincerely.

Riccardo Morandi

The correct appellation of a man capable of conceiving and building a structure is 'architect'

Pier Luigi Nervi

The work of Riccardo Morandi

Too much architecture, today, seems to be tending towards an expressionism which, turning its back on post-war structuralism, has become purely decorative. The spread of this fashion, which is often quite unjustifiable, and out of key with the requirements of the subject, tends to separate architecture from the 'functional aesthetic' by which a building, as such, should always be bound, and which is one of the few real achievements of architecture in this century.

The unwarranted licence expressed in the complicated and often excessively thin roofs designed geometrically rather than statically, or in the unnecessary size of some comparatively unimportant members, observed in the last few years, can only lead very quickly to an extension of 'Neo-Liberty' forms to all the structural elements of architecture, to the expenditure on a frivolous and purely graphic aestheticism of sums quite disproportionate to the economics of the work as a whole, and to passing off as original thought a useless and vulgar baroque which only displays the lack of a genuine architectural conscience.

Alongside this explicable but unjustifiable retrograde step in the 'art of construction', the measured activities of the few architects who still have true feelings and inspiration continue to bear more lasting fruit. We turned to their work when the spread of the above-mentioned ideas led us to make a close analytical study of this 'architecture' in order to understand the deeper reasons for these designs without being influenced by pre-conceived ideas. In order to analyse the objective validity of these works we examined them very closely, we photographed them, we re-designed them and re-faced them; we have willingly cancelled out the impression we had gained of them through the personality of those who had already studied and illustrated them; we have willingly separated them from the inevitable load of emotion springing from the graphic 'style' imposed on them by the designers themselves.

This book, therefore, dedicated to the work of Riccardo Morandi, is intended neither as criticism nor as biography, but simply to illustrate as objectively as possible the essential aspects of our investigations. In this we were guided partly by criteria of scientific research: and in order to support, and to communicate directly, without complicated phraseology, the clear results of our study, we have chosen to illustrate the text with the most 'objective' photographs and drawings from the many in our collection.

*　　　*　　　*

Nor should it seem strange, at this juncture, that to represent Architecture we should have chosen an engineer, which is how Riccardo Morandi is generally described. Once again it is, in fact, clear that among the more notable examples of contemporary architecture it is those created by engineers rather than by architects that are to be found in the first rank; obviously, not by mediocre engineers, who so often tend to be confused with and disguised as architects, without having their good qualities but only their defects, but by technically qualified engineers whose contribution to contemporary civilization is as undeniably outstanding as is the architectural validity of their work: Hennebique, Maillart, Perret, Nervi, and similar examples show this clearly enough.

The deep impression which these men have made on architecture, although they are to some extent outside the profession, is without doubt due to the new definition of problems involved in the 'art of construction', a definition which has been gradually crystallizing during the last century. Modern architecture, born of a violent expressionist explosion, has, in fact, become more and more orientated towards the new ideal of a balance between form and function, between statics and aesthetics, between economy and social ethics, together recognized as the necessary components of a perfect scheme: components never before, let us not say gone into thoroughly, but even touched on, as we are endeavouring, even if only in theory, to do today.

During the initial 'settling-down' period of the new architecture, which coincided with so many fundamental changes in the structure of society and with such remarkable advances in the applied sciences, it was inevitable that the more strictly 'technical' aspects of construction should take on maximum importance. They should, in fact, be in the hands of certain designers, sufficient to create valid examples of architecture, placing 'engineers' and 'architects' side by side in the broad highway of the 'art of construction'. These exceptional 'technicians' have, in fact, made a valid contribution to architecture on the plane of interpretation and knowledge of the structural material, at the same time that Frank Lloyd Wright, Mies van der Rohe, Gropius or Le Corbusier were making it on the plane of interpretation of contemporary thought, expressing it through architectural form, and thus through life itself.

This is why Riccardo Morandi, both as designer and as reinforced concrete technologist, has become an international authority in the architectural field. In common with the most able students of reinforced concrete structure, he saw the evolution of reinforced concrete as technique and as architecture, and has made a notable contribution towards transforming its original character of a simple means of construction into a genuine means of architectural expression, to be counted among the finest and the most worth-while.

In spite of his broad theoretical and technical background, his designs are not founded on abstract or formalistic concepts rigidly bound to structural theory or to technical data, but rather on a spontaneous intuition about the architectonic organism as a whole—an intuition which frees him, particularly in his more recent works, from that rigidity of thought which almost inevitably follows upon an extensive experience of construction.

Born and educated in Rome, where, while still young, he graduated as an engineer, Riccardo Morandi started his professional career in Calabria during the years immediately following the completion of his studies, with the design of reinforced concrete structures for new churches in the earthquake-prone district. This start had a strong formative influence upon him and it was this early work which confirmed him in his vocation.

When his work in Southern Italy came to an end, his apprenticeship continued and broadened during the next period of his work, in Rome, which was concerned with the study and solution of technical problems arising from the new types of structure which, between the wars, were spreading equally to building. His return to Rome, allied to the experience he had previously gained and the comparative absence of specialists in the field, led him, in fact, to devote himself entirely to an activity which seemed to him rich in promise for the future.

A close and broad-based collaboration with a reinforced concrete contractor, Magrini, and the desire to delve ever deeper into the technical aspect of the material, were deciding factors on his future, and gave him the solid basis of technological and theoretical knowledge of reinforced concrete structures which in recent years has enabled him to carry out works of great technical daring which are at the same time carefully worked out and tested from the point of view of form and of execution.

The fruits of such a solid basis of work were evident from the earliest years. With the church at Colleferro, near Rome, built in 1934 on a modest budget for Senator Parodi, reinforced concrete first gained recognition as a new medium of expression. The porch and campanile, built with exposed vertical reinforced concrete slabs of minimum thickness, clearly show, although still in conventional form, how mechanical calculations and the impersonal design of a purely load-bearing structure could not completely satisfy his 'sense of the material'. This work, the first, chronologically, which can be entirely attributed to Morandi architecturally as well as structurally, represents the starting point of a long research into aesthetics and function in close relationship with the nature of 'his' material.

But notwithstanding this first statement, the true formative process cannot yet be said to be complete. Alongside the Colleferro church, and for the few years immediately following that work, there came those numerous purely technical works which gradually led to his being appreciated by the close-knit society of Roman 'constructors'. Cinemas and factories were the recurring themes of these early years of his work in Rome—themes closely related both to the notable structural contribution of reinforced concrete and to originality of structural design : themes difficult both architecturally and technically, owing to the novelty both of the means of construction and of the 'subject' to be dealt with.

The architectonic expression of these works, however, was almost entirely dependent upon the solution of a functional problem, but, notwithstanding the simplicity and spareness of their shapes, their realization necessitated a constant battle with clients and contractors who were not yet ready for the new expression and lacked the technical knowledge which would have enabled them to understand and judge them fairly, and who therefore thought them to be excessively daring and complicated.

The lack of understanding of his work which Morandi met with in the years immediately before the Second World War, both on the plane of execution and of technical research (his earliest thoughts and investigations on prestressed concrete go back to 1936) while stimulating him to persevere (they gave him a sense of prescience) gradually compelled him to confine himself more and more to the narrow field of reinforced concrete 'calculator' and of the 'expert in piled foundations' as he came to be known at that time, and to which the schools of his day had trained him, restricting himself to being an intermediary between the architectural concept and structural requirements.

His youthful collaboration with the 'architects' often had its bitter moments because they could not understand that the 'calculator' might be aware of the possibilities of expression offered by the material which he had learned to deal with on the technical plane. In this respect it may be interesting to refer to what Morandi recently had to say about his 'human' experiences during the early years of his career:

'The residue of a positivist mentality, a technical literature, largely German, founded on a tabulated casuistry, brought about a state of affairs in which no work for which the chief engineer was also the chief architect (the Forth bridge, Eiffel's Truyère viaduct at Garabit, Maillart's bridges, Freyssinet's Orly hangars, Hennebique's Risorgimento bridge in Rome, Nervi's early works) even entered into the considerations of critics or men of culture. These were still engaged in discussion of Vignola's styles and their application—even though below the tympani and the classical arches there was hidden a robust, reinforced concrete beam which performed the entire static function. Our generation has had to free itself from the effects of a training falsified by prejudices and erroneous distinctions, in order to achieve its own individual style, relying mainly, but not entirely, on intuition, the feeling for structure and the possibility of finding the confirmation of its own inventions in calculation. But calculation, that mysterious word to the uninitiated, and in whose name so many fine projects have been, and are constantly being, ruined, can never be considered as a finally determining factor in the form of a structure, when it can be clearly demonstrated that this last is dependent on the sensibility and knowledge of the designer, whether he be architect or engineer.'

But the passion which Morandi brought to his work, and which came of his deep conviction that it could place him among the most constructive of Italian architects, was not wasted: his time came at the end of the war.

The national reconstruction effort found him, in fact, firmly placed among those recognized as responsible for this work, and gave him, in addition, the opportunity of plunging into problems which were deeply congenial to him, a field in which he had been able to regain the lost ground in one bound: bridges. These, in fact, gave him the best possible opportunity to place himself squarely among the most highly appreciated of Italian designers. Scores of bridges have been designed in his studio during the last fifteen years, and slowly but surely, through a constant upsurge of his own innermost capacity, these structures have taken on new shapes and personalities, ever more appreciated by clients and contractors alike, particularly during the early post-war years, when joy in work and in the ideas which accompanied the so-called 'Italian Renaissance' were the order of the day.

The authority thus so hardly won over thirty years of hard and passionate work—an authority based on an uncommonly serious training—could not fail to bring with it international recognition of the worth of Riccardo Morandi as technologist and as architect. This recognition became even more firmly established of recent years with the construction of some outstanding works in Italy and abroad: from the Storms River Bridge in South Africa to that over Lake Maracaibo in Venezuela and the Polcevera viaduct at Genoa; from the project for the Sports City in Teheran to that for saving the Egyptian temples of Abu Simbel in Nubia, and to the buildings for the Fiumicino International Airport in Rome. But all these works, even the most recent, cannot actually be said to represent the conclusion of an experience, or the codification of a style in academic terms. They are rather the sincere and free expression of a henceforth unfettered imagination, and the beginning of a highly constructive activity on behalf of architecture, allied to a still incredibly fertile professional maturity.

*   *   *

Riccardo Morandi has always been able, as have few other designers, to envisage the requirements and opportunities of modern civilization in concrete architectural terms, and, without his own contracting business which would have enabled him to treat his works with much greater freedom and daring, he has always known how to overcome opposition to the new standards of construction he has suggested, strong in his own deep knowledge of the project and of the problems relating to its execution. He never leaves anything either at the design or the construction stage to the responsibility of his assistants, though they are many, and highly qualified : himself the designer and calculator of his own schemes, he personally looks after their execution, enriching his experience in this way, day by day, and making continual and careful stylistic advances.

An enemy to improvisation and superficiality, Morandi never thinks it right to have to tackle a new scheme in an unorthodox way. The economic and time factors are to him too important, because they can too easily be sacrificed to uncontrolled flights of fancy. He considers unjustifiable any unnecessary expenditure of energy and resources on controversial and formal experiments, the success of which cannot be guaranteed even by the designer himself.

From the very first he studied the various problems methodically, proposing, in the first instance, solutions which, while they were not actually familiar, still made no definite contribution to the development of architecture. Then gradually, from the first modest examples, as more and more commissions for the type of work he had already designed rolled in, he began to part company with tradition whenever it seemed to him that the time was ripe to adopt new and progressive variants in form and method, variants which, although comparatively untried generally, he himself had already gone into thoroughly and studied with the greatest care.

This method of working is evident in the development of the forms and technique of his bridge designs—a development in which a decisive element was the technological factor which entered into the new solutions, giving them a well-founded structural originality. The various static designs he gradually adopted led to a continual, and notable, increase in the length of spans, a far greater delicacy in the beams and a greater spring in the arches, and to the different forces of compression and tension being the primary reason for modifications of dimensions, shapes and inclination of the various members, showing in this way the expressive possibilities of structures which had generally been restrained and circumscribed.

This slow reaching after the truth, undertaken with special care in the case of structure, but always sought for in the architectural field as well, is evident from a look at the solutions he proposed and carried out for the various schemes entrusted to him—solutions which we have tried to represent in the following pages, together with detailed descriptions of some of the more significant, and some hitherto unpublished, works.

Besides this, Morandi's 'structuralism', if we can call it that, is directly related to an accepted architectural premise which can be readily appreciated from an analysis of the most significant works of architecture of the past : that it is always, and only, the structure of a building that provides a valid basis for the formal and decorative aspect of the work. Arches, columns, beams, trusses, have always performed, plainly and usefully, the dual function of 'supporting' and 'decorating'; the sculptural and plastic richness of the façade and the interior has always been expressed so naturally in forms derived from the structural elements that when this is not the case, there is always a decline of true architectural creativity and a sterile play of useless decorations. The indissoluble link between form and structural function is, in the last analysis, one of the most concrete and most immediately obvious links among the many which are intertwined in architecture, and the ignoring of which has always led to a complete misrepresentation of the problem of construction.

The intimate connection between this architectural-structural functionalism and the distributive-economic functionalism, which is increasingly present in the mind of those who practice the profession of architecture, can only, today, lead to a return to the concept of certain mediaeval and renaissance models which, with the right proportions, are highly topical even today. The rationalism and moderation of their design would, in fact, eliminate at the outset two of the biggest stumbling blocks to the development of the new forms of architecture, represented on the one hand by illogical attempts to make of the load-bearing structure a forced and complex pretext for ornamental motifs (quite apart from any consideration of economics, and the more useless when the further removed from structural necessity) and, on the other hand, by the carelessness with which the structures are often studied and introduced into the architecture, almost as if their use were dictated by some shameful necessity, unworthy of the name of Art.

Conscious of the fundamental importance of the structure in all construction work, and convinced, moreover, that if a work of architecture is to have value the problems related to it cannot be solved by expediency either on the technical or the architectural plane, Morandi, as we have said before, devoted his early years—those of his most intense spiritual development—to the strictly technical field of calculation, and particularly to the technology of materials, forcing himself, by the complexity of the problems to be solved and his constant pursuit of progress, to a long and obscure apprenticeship, both formative and informative—the inevitable price to be paid by anyone who wishes to make a positive contribution, in ideas and achievement, to contemporary civilization.

It should cause no surprise, therefore, that of the thirty years of his professional life it is only the second half which shows real detachment from technical rigidity and pure technology, and his ever-deepening understanding of the formal problems of architectural expression.

In view of this highly specialized training, bridges could not fail to be an ideal subject for Morandi from all points of view. Their pure and clearly defined structure—an expression of true form, stylistically completely itself— found in him one of the few people able to express themselves naturally through useful and logical shapes, the enemies of compromise and half-measures which, on the other hand, so easily thrive in the soil of architecture, which is so much richer, and for this very reason less straightforward and more unbalanced. And this definite 'structural' position that he took up, courageously, with all its implications, he also attributed to the industrial buildings, the cinemas, the hangars, built in his time, and indissolubly linked to the rich, deep experience of the bridge builder.

Fundamentally, therefore, the basis of all his work—that which differentiates it so clearly from that of contemporary architects and gives it so much in common with that of the greatest representatives of the 'art of construction'—remains the sincerity of expression of his structures. These perhaps are at times a little too crude, owing to the over-emphasized tendency to large spans and great internal stresses. Nonetheless they always appear in shapes of disconcerting sincerity and clarity, revealing an unusually powerful structural inspiration.

This essentially positive aspect of his work obviously has its reverse side. In his building the immediate excitement of construction has rarely allowed him time to carry to the limits the abstract sense of composition inherent in certain juxtapositions of voids and volumes—to give to their relationships the long and careful study it deserved, or to make immediately plain the correspondence between the basic architectural idea and the concrete form in which it is expressed.

But if, on the one hand, this is due to this professional 'correctness' in refusing to admit of delay in carrying out the many tasks required of him, on the other hand, it cannot be denied that it is partly due to his 'Latin passion' for building. A coldly, critical objectivity and a fertile imagination march badly together, the more so when the designer turns away, like Morandi, from theorizing that is not strictly technical and objective and declares himself to be 'neither a philosopher nor a critic', giving in this way confirmation of his strength as an architect.

If on the one hand, however, these refining processes result from a long study of the subject, they are, on the other hand, often a sign of a spiritual heritage divorced from experience, which may be either accepted or rejected, but which is always acquired during the formative years, in the course of collaboration. The scale and urgency of his design work during his most fertile years, however, led to many of Morandi's works seeming more like the concrete expression of a thought than an elaborate discourse, and his youthful estrangement from the schools and from the accepted currents of professional studies, which saved him from imitative formalism, none the less condemned him to a slow and lonely search for style, carried on more through successive jobs that he undertook than through successive versions of a single job. The influence which has been observed in some of his works, therefore, is not due to a pupil's recollections but to a series of original attempts to achieve a formal result.

To fully understand Riccardo Morandi's architecture, it is necessary to remember the importance of the 'execution' factor: the necessity, which he himself recognizes, to use mechanical means as an auxiliary to human labour. Only in this way, in fact, was it possible for him to apply those advanced constructional techniques which enabled him to achieve the spectacular results we have noted—results which are more at one with architecture than with technology—such as the construction of the slender bridges over the Storms River and the Lussia, with a single arch built without the aid of centering, and the construction of the immeasurably harmonious horizontal beams, precast off the site and placed by 'launching', as used for the Quercia Setta Viaduct on the Autostrada del Sole, or for the more recent bridge over Lake Maracaibo. This last example shows how, though restricted by coldly objective conditions, he was able to reject purely mechanistic solutions and use his great technical knowledge to further the architectural ideal closest to the Latin spirit, turning from abstract (even if perfect) formal solutions *à la Mies van der Rohe* and maintaining in his constructions, including buildings, that 'visual solidity' so foreign to many architects of today.

In all that we have tried to demonstrate up to now, it is clear that the spaces and the volumes defined by Riccardo Morandi's structures can never be regarded as either a visible concretizing of the interpenetration between interior and exterior, or as a functional abstraction in the purely geometric, or static, sense. But they carry within themselves their own conclusion and justification according to the most deep-rooted traditional Latin-European concepts of architecture, which are the more vital today since the spirit of man, deprived of its inherent tranquility, is harried on all sides by disruptive forces. The need to reduce this mad chase to an abstract, albeit unconscious and standardized community of thought, is something Morandi feels so strongly that even his structures (as opposed to buildings) are so closely related to nature around—and to it alone—that they form themselves into elements of a landscape—though in contrast to their own immediate surroundings.

The general views we have chosen to illustrate some of the works collected here show this clearly.

Nonetheless, Morandi is one of the few obvious examples of a refusal of technocracy for its own sake just as much as of the vain aesthetic solutions, synthesized *a postiori* in a supposed union of the classic components of construction : technique, function and form. The balance between these elements springs directly from his work and is never a forced compromise between the strictly functional standpoint, the rigid static solution and the architectural composition. The absence in him of a preconceived structural formalism, however, keeps him from irrational and mechanical solutions, while the simple dignity of his design, and its strict and genuine structural expressiveness, lead him to a clear and living architecture, closely related to the tasks required of it. And it is precisely in this that the great importance of Riccardo Morandi lies—as has appeared ever more clearly during our research on his work—in having known, that is, how to concretize ideas which can be taught, and how to demonstrate an art which, while it remains the expression of a definite personality is, nonetheless, clearly intelligible and communicable.

Intrados of one of the spans of the Quercia Setta viaduct

This bridge in the Paguita quarter of Caracas, where an important new road overpasses a section of the city built in a valley, is one of the most important works carried out by the Venezuelan Government. The new bridge spans a river and, at one end, a wide avenue which it had to overpass without the work causing interruption to the flow of traffic.

The problem was therefore fairly complicated and its solution had, besides, to comply with a number of functional requirements without disturbing the appearance of the surrounding neighbourhood. Riccardo Morandi, however, succeeded in achieving a singularly expressive architectural result without having recourse to any structural falsification.

The bridge, which is largely constructed in prestressed concrete, consists of a shallow cellular arch with a span of 295 ft. and a rise of 24 ft. 4 in., the structure of which is extended beyond the side piers by straight beams resting on the abutments and forming with the centre span a clearly expressed static and visual whole, and giving two 65 ft. 6 in. side spans with the avenue passing below one of them.

The work is on a marked skew in relation to the line of the banks, and

Morandi has used this characteristic to create an original architectural feature, showing clearly on the soffit the construction of the arch. In fact, this skew, which gave rise to a number of major structural difficulties (since there was an angle of 60 degrees between the bridge and the water-course and parallel road), was the determining factor in the design of the central arch and the side spans. These are constructed with a series of independent cellular ribs, actually identical to one another but designed, from the point of view of appearance, in accordance with the line of the land level below.

The deck, supported on a series of small raking columns which counteract the horizontal component of the thrust of the arch, is in ordinary reinforced concrete, while the central arch is prestressed. The use of prestressed concrete was dictated by the large bending moments in the area of loading caused by the extreme shallowness of the arch.

As can be seen, this structure has produced rich and lively effects of colour and light and shade, which, besides giving the work its very definite character, contribute to the architectural expression of the structural basis of the work—the independent arches which act together in successive and clearly defined sectors.

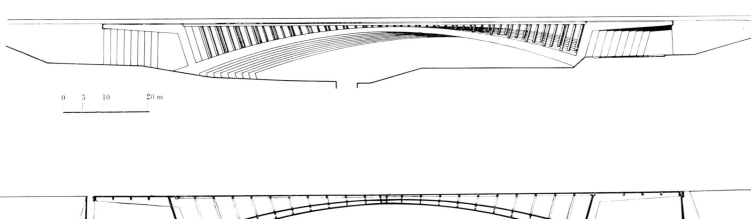

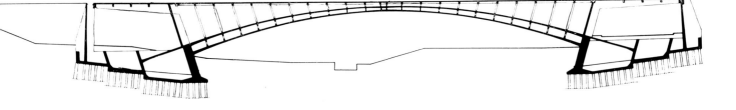

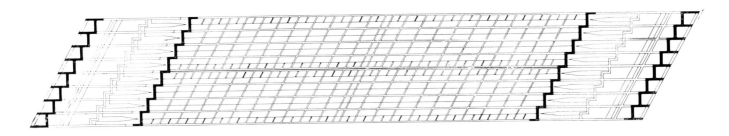

Elevation, longitudinal section and plan of the deck soffit

26

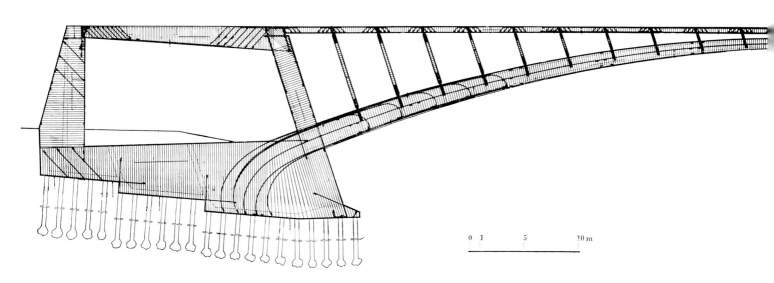

Longitudinal section through the reinforcement of one of the modular skew elements of the Nueva Republica bridge

0 1   5   10 m

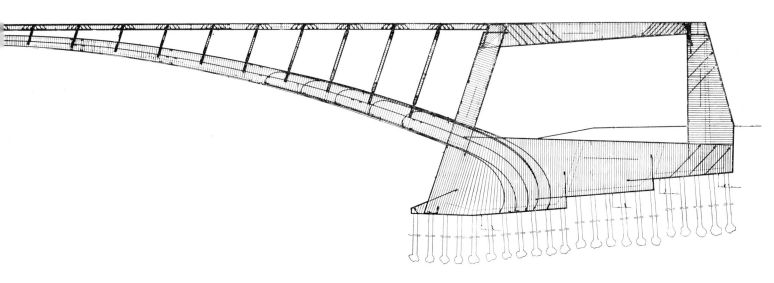

The Lussia footbridge

hese bridges represent a highly important stage in Morandi's udies on single arch structures : particularly important, indeed, as was governed by the special requirements of each project, alough the three had a common type of structure and an architecral outline strictly in accordance with it.

otbridge over the Lussia. In the first case, at Garfagnana, a footidge was required to span one of the arms of a recently-construced hydryo-electric reservoir. Riccardo Morandi solved the problem ith a three-pinned arch with a 230 ft. span plus a prestressed conete deck carried on two T-frames each forming two 72 ft. 4 in. ans.

he footbridge itself thus consists of two pairs of T-frames joined ansversely at three points : at one end at the abutment, at their entre point by two vertical 69 ft. high supports, and at their other her end at the key of the arch, on which they rest. The transverse embers of the frames consist of ribs each $6\frac{1}{2}$ in. thick and 4 ft. eep, linked by a thin slab and a series of thin transverse members in ne with the zone of negative moment, which are carried on a soffit ab of varying thickness.

hese transverse members were precast and prestressed. The olution adopted for the arch, on the other hand, is unusual in this pe of structure, Riccardo Morandi having adopted a special ethod of placing dictated by considerations of economy. The eat height between the bottom of the reservoir and the key of the ch, not less than the nature of the soil, would have made the conruction of centering particularly difficult, and quite disproportion-

ate to the scale of the work. Not only that, but the programme of construction of the hydro-electric plant made it clear that the filling of the reservoir would have seriously impeded the recovery of the lower part of the centering, which would have been gradually submerged during the course of the work. Morandi therefore decided to construct two half-arches on the adjoining hillside, which could be positioned by rotating them on hinges ; this rotation would not need to take place simultaneously on both sides, as this would have necessitated excessively complicated machinery and equipment.

To rotate them one at a time, on the other hand, it was sufficient to provide a central tubular steel tower in line with the key of the arch, which would serve as a temporary support to the half-arch placed first, while, using the same equipment, the rotation of the second half-arch was proceeded with.

To enable the structure to withstand the varying stresses to which it would be subjected during the different stages of rotation, without increasing the size and reinforcement of the arch beyond the economic limit, Morandi thought it advisable to apply a temporary prestress which would enable the three-pinned arch to support a concentrated load in the zone nearest the crown, and which would counteract the tensile stresses in the whole length of the structure, by means of a series of top and bottom cables, the tension in which could be varied according to the position of the half-arch.

This elaborate concept, moreover, did not require any specially complicated equipment. The Vagli di Sotto footbridge is thus a rare example of slenderness and harmonious lines, apparently obtained without effort and seemingly almost by a stroke of happy intuition.

31

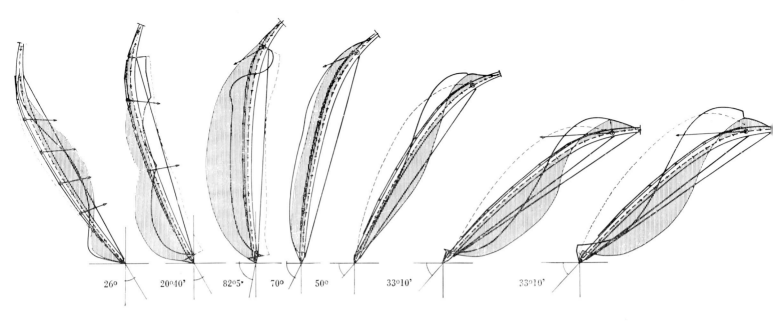

26°   20°40'   82°5'   70°   50°   33°10'   33°10'

Diagrams of the bending moments in a half-arch of the Lussia footbridge; hatched—those due to the load on rotation; dotted lines—those due to induced tension (variable pre-tension of the extrados and intrados cables); solid lines—those due to the resultant moment

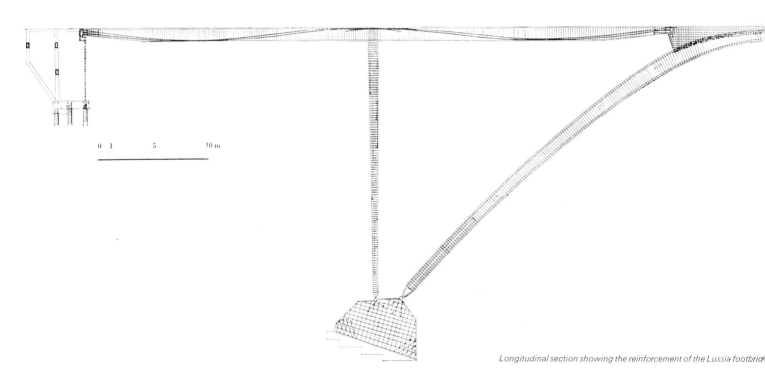

0 1   5   10 m

Longitudinal section showing the reinforcement of the Lussia footbridge

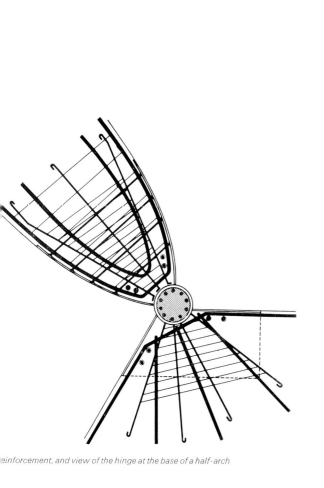

einforcement, and view of the hinge at the base of a half-arch

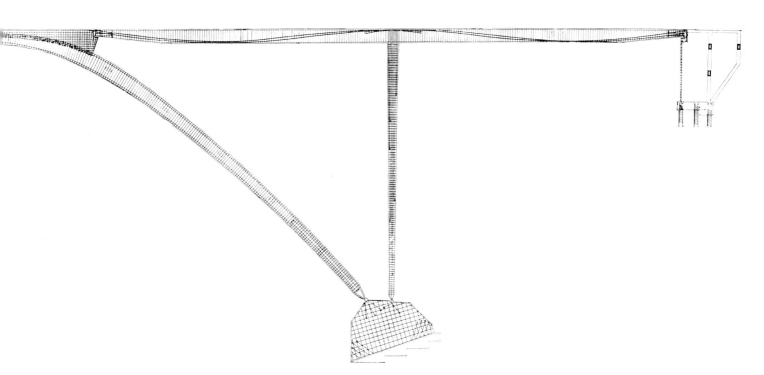

33

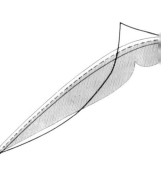

Longitudinal section . .

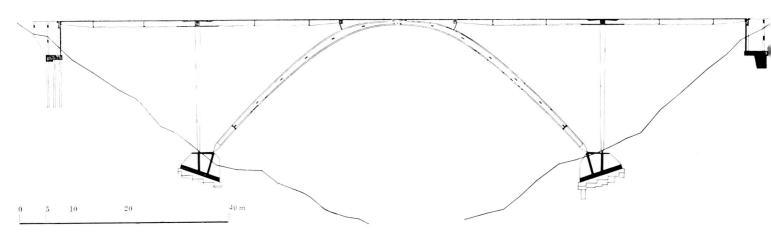

| 0 | 5 | 10 | 20 | 40 m |

34

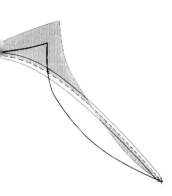

...grams of the maximum bending moments due to the load distributed over ... whole arch (in solid lines) and to those distributed only over the right ...d arch (hatched)

...o stages in the rotation of a half-arch; the photograph shows the variable-...stress cables and those used for the application of tension to the winches

torms River bridge. A similar scheme, to comply with similar conditions, was adopted by Morandi for the design of the bridge
carried out for the National Highway Administration of South
Africa, across a deep gorge of the Storms River. Here the config-
uration of the site was the deciding factor in choosing a construction without centering for an arch of 328 ft. span, and the introduction of a special arrangement of the supporting columns of the
deck in order to make a notable reduction in the forces acting on the
arch, as was seen in the Paguita viaduct. In view of the size and
heavy loadings, the arch was divided, for construction purposes,
into four sections, of which the two nearest the springing, each of
which is about 31 ft. 6 in. long, were cast *in situ* with ordinary
centering, while the two central sections, each about 147 ft. 6 in.
long, were constructed vertically on reinforced concrete frames and,
subsequently, rotated simultaneously round temporary hinges until
they met at the crown of the arch. The temporary hinges placed at
the base of the rotating sections were fixed as soon as the rotation
was completed, and the reinforced concrete frames demolished, so
that the arch takes on its final character of a continuous structure
built into the abutments.

The arch, which has a span of 328 ft. and a height of 65 ft. 6 in., is a
closed cellular structure 23 ft. deep at the springing and 20 ft. 6 in. at
the crown, consisting of a pair of thin slabs at extrados and intrados
with a thickness varying from 12 in. to 17 in., and of four longitudinal ribs varying in thickness from 8 ft. at the springing to 4 ft. at
the crown. The deck, which was calculated to withstand the British
standard moving load, is carried on three independent structures:
two lateral ones, consisting of continuous beams of seven 33-ft.
spans, resting on specially-shaped raking columns founded on the
ground, and a similar central system with continuous beams with
five spans, of lengths varying according to their position in the arch.

It may be of interest to give here the successive phases of construction of the work:

1) Construction of the sections of the arch nearest to the springing, and of the temporary frames.

2) Construction of the lateral lengths of deck.

3) Construction of the two rotation sections of the arch which
   occur between the crown and the temporary hinges, in an
   almost vertical position.

4) Rotation of the hinged portions of the arch.

5) Completion of the construction of the arch.

6) Completion of the deck on top of the arch.

As the illustrations show, the basic characteristic of the bridge consists in the inclined arrangement of the columns, which transmit the
load from the deck to the arch and so to the ground in the statically
most useful way (counteracting, by their inclined thrust, the eccentricity of the thrust along the arch itself) and which give to the whole
work a remarkable character of lightness, accentuated by the effec-
tive unity in the design of the principal members.

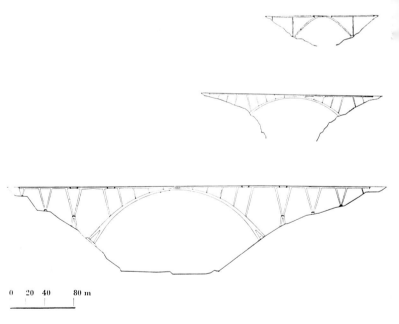

0   20   40   80 m

Elevations of the Lussia footbridge, the Storms River bridge and the Fiumarella viaduct

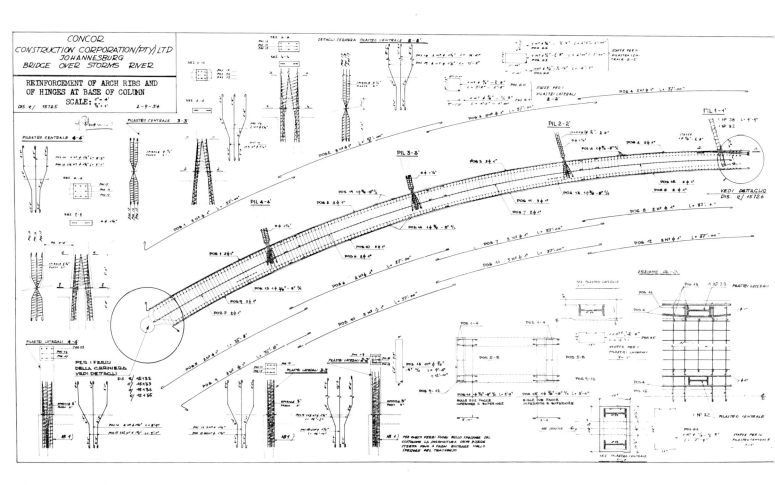

pilastro centrale (laterale)/centre (side) column : dettagli cerniera/details of hinge : staffe per/ stirrups for : sulle due facce inferiore e superiore /on lower and upper faces : per questi ferri fuori spessore del costolone la sagomatura deve essere stretta fino a farli entrare nello spessore del trasverso/ these bars, which are outside the thickness of the large ribs, must be carefully shaped to bring them within the thickness of the transverse beams

Reinforcement of the ribs of the Storms River bridge and of the temporary hinges at the base
(original working drawing)

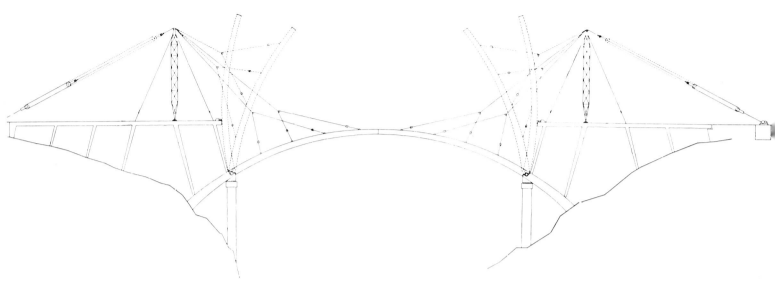

Sketch showing the stages in the 'launching' of the central portion of the arch

Longitudinal section

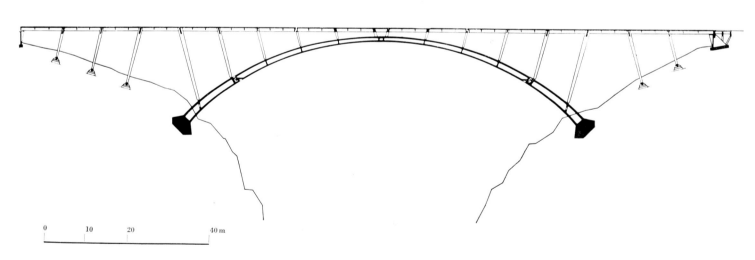

0	10	20		40 m

...ree stages in the simultaneous rotation of the two half-arches

...tail of the reinforcement of the temporary rotation hinge

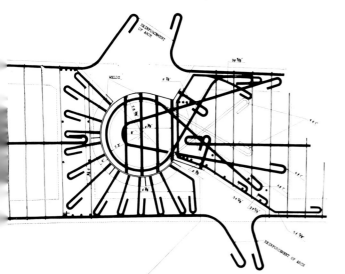

Fiumarella viaduct. The latest of the bridges of this type designed by Morandi is that recently completed to link the town of Catanzaro with the Strada dei Due Mari (Two-Seas Road) across the valley of the Fiumarella : of the three works described it is, undoubtedly, the most impressive.

The connecting road planned would have had to cross the valley at a level approximately 360 ft. above the river bed, requiring a span of approximately 1,542 ft., and in view of the steepness of the valley sides, the structure would therefore have had to be of exceptional size. Not only that, but the great depth of the valley and the fact that the foundation soil is of an alluvial nature while the sides of the valley are solid rock, made it advisable for obvious reasons of economy to reduce to a minimum the vertical supports of the bridge.

After his previous experience, therefore, the solution proposed by Morandi could only be the following : a reinforced concrete arch with a theoretical rise of about 216 ft. and a theoretical span of about 760 ft., carrying a deck with a carriageway at the level 301.50m. (989 ft.), supported on inclined columns borne in part on the arch and in part on the sides of the valley : columns which, with their inclination to the vertical, would take care of the horizontal component in the way most favourable to the stability of the arch.

Essentially, therefore, the structural design of both arch and deck repeats that of the Storms River bridge, though with different dimensions and thicknesses. What, on the other hand, is new and outstanding is the formal solution adopted for the ends of the arch, and the shape of the longitudinal beams and the inclined columns (which in this case are linked transversely)—a shape determined after a careful study of the relationship between the various members, and by a rational arrangement which, in our opinion, had led to a great expressiveness. For example, the arch is composed of two cellular and independent arches placed side by side and rigidly tied together, increasing in thickness towards the springing so that the depth of the work is least (33 ft. 6 in.) at the crown and greatest (82 ft.) at the springing. Moreover, each arch, in the area nearest the springing, is divided in its turn into two independent branches with an opening between them of 72 ft.

The 'boxes' forming the body of the arch are crossed by transverse members equal in number to the number of supports carrying the deck, and the ends of these at the crown are designed independently so as not to upset its elastic behaviour. The abutments, moreover, rest on the ground through the medium of two cellular distribution plates which are square on plan, with 82 ft. sides, positioned on an inclined plane normal to the geometric axis of the arch.

The deck consists of four parallel ribs with a width varying from 9 in. to 2 ft. 3 in. and a depth varying from 4 ft. 10 in. to 7 ft. 9 in., joined by a top slab 6 in. thick and by thin transverse stiffening diaphragms each 6 in. wide and 3 ft. 3 in. deep, and varying in section with the supports. These transverse diaphragms, together with the two rows of inclined, varying-section columns, together form a frame with a variable moment of inertia.

The load-bearing structure formed by the arch and deck was calculated by traditional methods. Here, too, the use of the inclined supports reduces the thrust at the crown by means of a horizontal action which considerably reduces its eccentricity, besides reducing the height of the supports themselves and making it possible to construct them without wind bracing. The difference between the two shells, moreover, leads to a high resistance to horizontal wind action (which is strong in this region) and to a good distribution of the load over a wide foundation area.

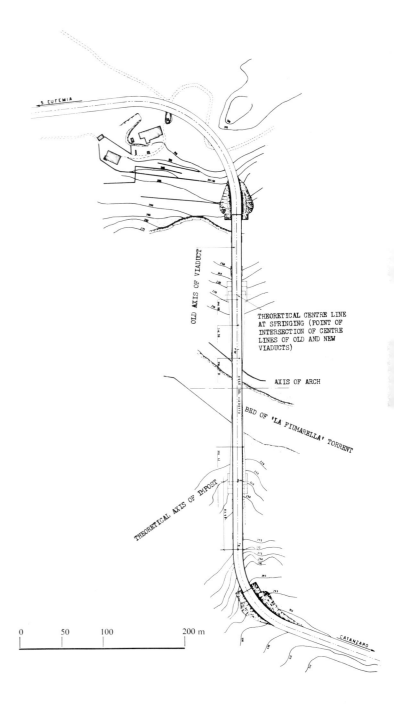

General layout of the Fiumarella viaduct. **Opposite:** *tubular steel scaffolding for the main arch of the viaduct, seen from below*

43

Details of the base and crown hinges

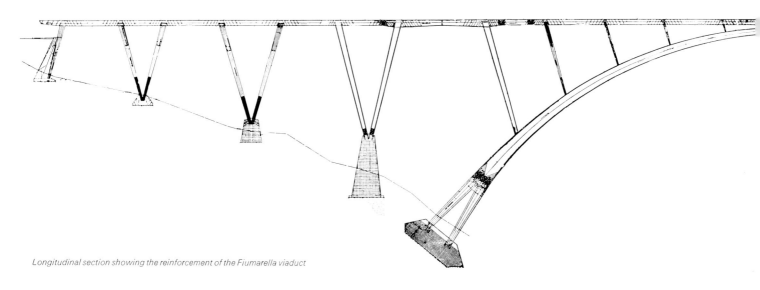

Longitudinal section showing the reinforcement of the Fiumarella viaduct

44

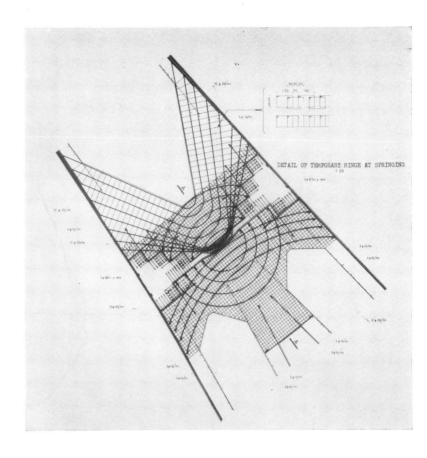

DETAIL OF TEMPORARY HINGE AT SPRINGING
1:20

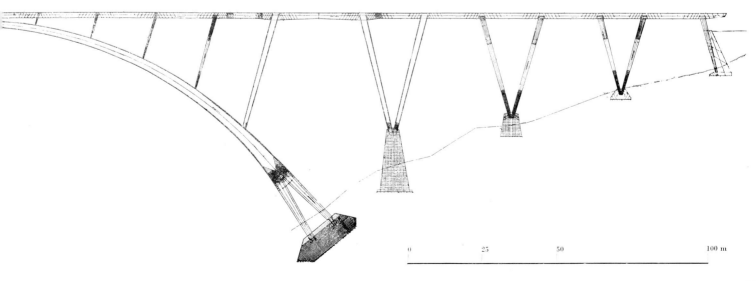

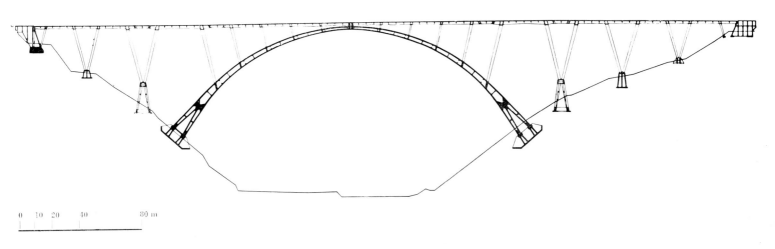

n of the viaduct and longitudinal section: below: diagram of the temporary scaffolding

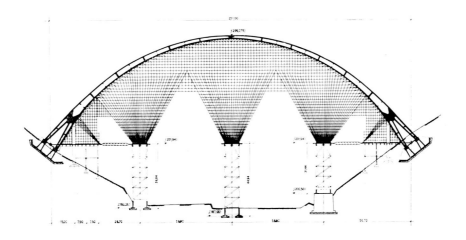

49

marella viaduct

Underground hall in Valentino Park.

wo projects, two versions of the same interesting and difficult subject: a large, permanent exhibition hall with well-defined characteristics. A subject with very few fixed requirements, or at least, only those concerned with the maximum distance between the external walls and the maximum internal clear space free from supports. And these requirements Morandi has dealt with with outstanding results.

Underground hall in the Valentino Park, Turin. The first of these projects arose when the Turin Exhibition Authority found it necessary to build a large new hall in the Valentino Park to house the exhibition of industrial vehicles in connection with the annual Motor show, Nervi's original fine halls having become inadequate for the increased size of the exhibition. There immediately arose, however, the problem of the site of the new hall, which could not be accommodated in the small park without sacrificing a great proportion of the amenity. It was, therefore, suggested that the entire hall should be built below ground, under the area previously used for riding, and be linked with the existing halls by means of an underground passage; the surface would then be entirely reinstated and turned into a children's playground.

The new building was to consist of a single large hall 226 ft. wide and 490 ft. long, and to have its floor 26 ft. below normal ground level. At each end there had to be two road links so arranged as to have the long sides of the building in contact with the earth leaving the glazed ends open on to wide green amphitheatre-like slopes.

A suitable thickness of earth was to be placed on the roof in order to reinstate the planting of the surface with flower beds and small trees. This garden would be at very nearly the same level as the original parkland, and would be one with the gardens around, so that the new work would introduce no discordant note into the surroundings.

The characteristic load-bearing structure chosen by Morandi for the roof as a whole consists of pairs of ribs, placed 10 ft. 3 in. apart and carried on pairs of inclined piers at 36 ft. centres. The most characteristic aspect of the work lies in the arrangement of the slender ribs. These are, in fact, not placed parallel to the transvers axis of the

structure, but span the hall diagonally with two pairs of ribs resting on each pair of piers.

This arrangement was adopted by Morandi to solve the problem of the roof by a 'space frame' technique, with the large number of intersecting ribs eliminating any elastic instability in the very slender ribs without the use of any system of stiffeners or any possibility of transverse deformation of the roof from an excess of horizontal thrust.

All the ribs are 6 in. thick, increasing slightly where they meet the supports; their depth varies from a minimum of 4 ft. 3 in. to a maximum of 10 ft. 3 in. The horizontal infilling between the ribs follows a curve which provides for a good shedding of rainwater; it consists of a slab of reinforced brick with a thickness varying from $17\frac{1}{2}$ in. to $9\frac{1}{2}$ in.

The entire structure is in prestressed concrete and its special shape enables it to carry in the most efficient way the heavy load of the earth topping and any foreseeable accidental load. As was said above, the load is carried to the ground by means of large inclined, prestressed piers, tied by smaller struts to the side walls which are also in prestressed concrete. These walls have the double duty of retaining the earth along the sides of the building and acting with the load-bearing structure of the roof to provide a rigidity not inherent in the hinged supports.

The reason for the inclined piers, which provide components which reduce the bending moment in the roof, and for the intersecting ribs, which provide strong ties in every direction, is easy to see in view of the requirements of the work. These include large spans to leave clear open space for the exhibition of large vehicles; high external loadings due to the earth topping; notable pressure from the earth sides; need to reduce the height of the hall to facilitate access to the upper level.

A final glance at the finishings of the hall: all the structural members, inside and out, are in exposed board-marked concrete; the roof infilling is similarly exposed; no plastering or other finishing material has been introduced; the floor is paved in dark veined marble.

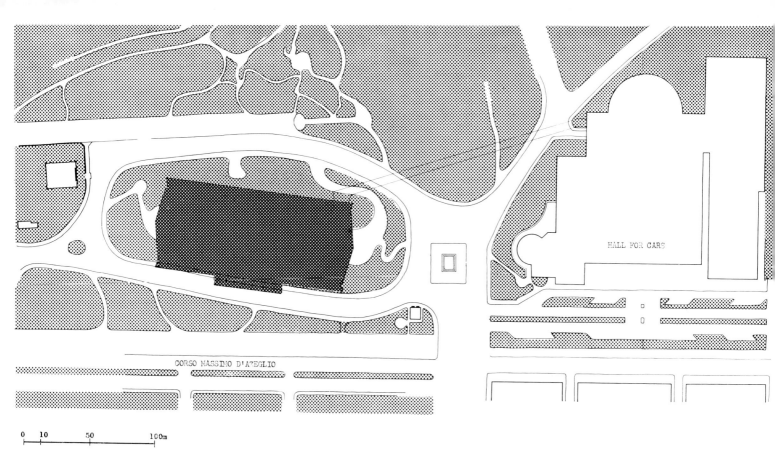

CORSO MASSIMO D'AZEGLIO

HALL FOR CARS

0 10   50   100m

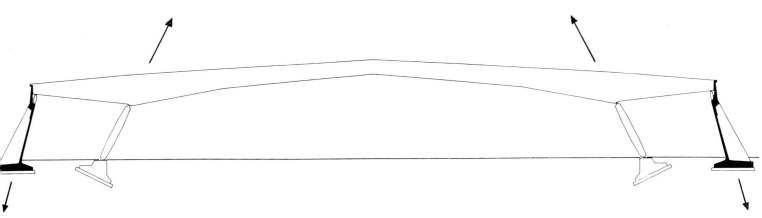

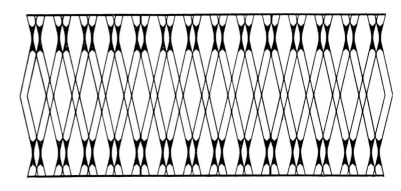

...atic design, and plan of the roof soffit of the underground hall

55

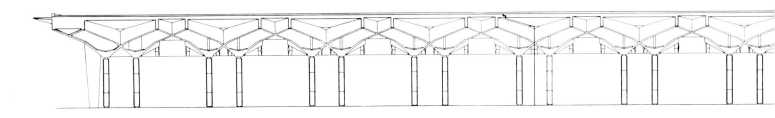

Longitudinal section

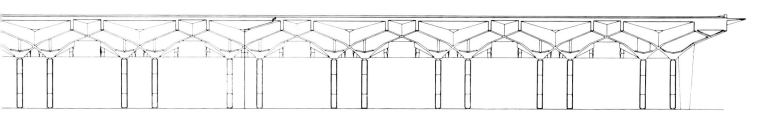

Stiffening slabs to the roof beams, close to the supports

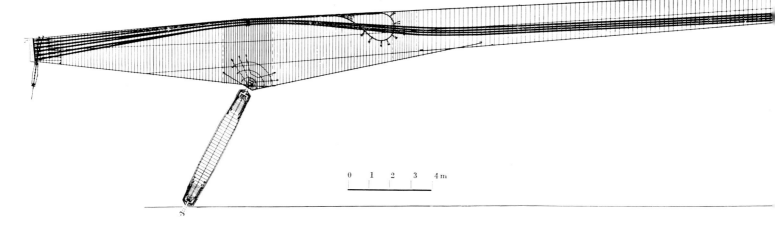

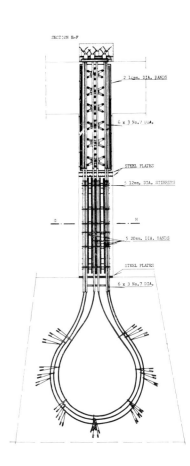

Top: longitudinal section of the beam system: **Left:** two views of the site, showing the construction of the formwork, resting on the earth which was used in place of scaffolding. Excavation was only carried out for the inclined supports. **Below:** reinforcement of the abutment ends of the supports.

Right: reinforcement of the supports and detail of the anchorage of the prestressing cables of the roof beams, prior to concreting

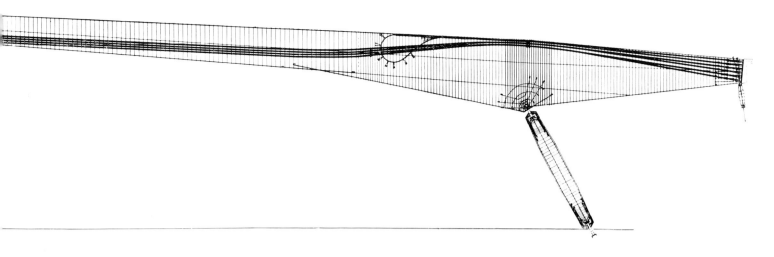

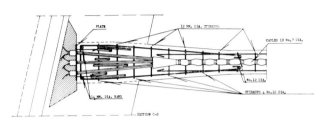

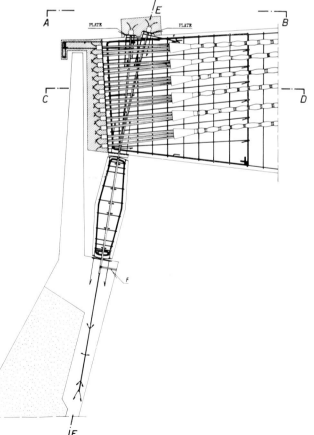

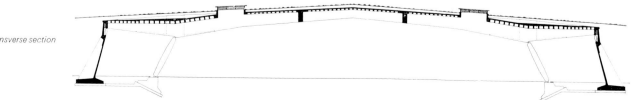

ansverse section

63

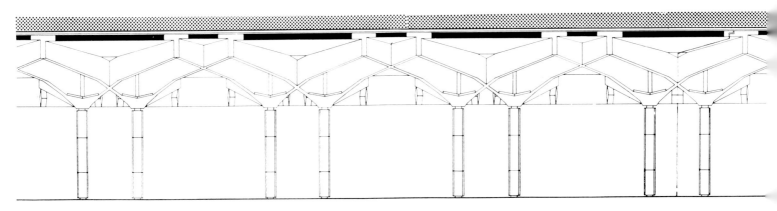

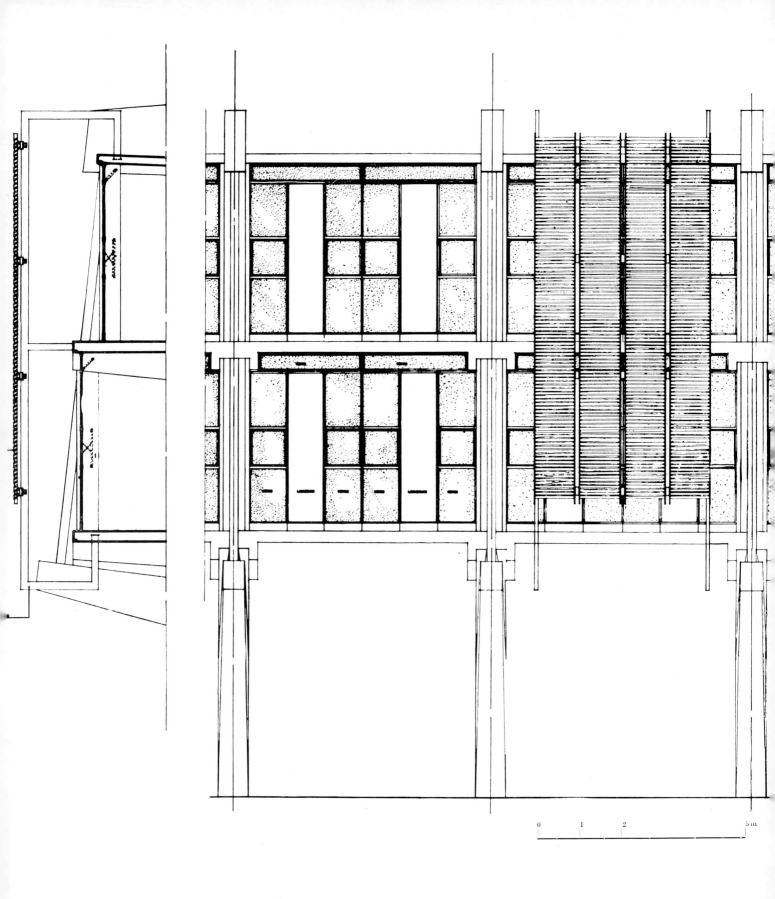

Original detail drawing of the side elevation of the Palace of Labo

66

Project for Palace of Labour. The second of these two subjects, which to a great extent duplicates the requirements of the first, is familiar, and P. L. Nervi's solution to it is well known. It was also for Turin, but for the district above the Corso Polonia, and for a building designed to house, first, the International Exhibition of Labour during the exhibition put on to celebrate the Centenary of Italian Unity and, subsequently, the National Centre for Professional Education.

To say this, is sufficient to convey all the difficulty attending the design of a building intended to be used for two such dissimilar functions without having to undergo any special modification or reconstruction.

The first use—for the International Exhibition of Labour—required a large hall designed on lines which would demonstrate Italian technical progress.

The obvious solution to this first problem seemed to be the adoption of a thin concrete shell roof (as has been done in many other European countries for covering such large areas) but Morandi did not feel that this would be entirely suitable. It would, in fact, have necessitated the use of heavy reinforcement, as well as imposing considerable height on the roof because of the large area to be covered, and such a height would have looked wrong in the surrounding townscape.

On the other hand, precisely over the last few years, some outstanding work has been done in Italy on large ribbed roofs, and this seemed the right solution to the second requirement of the building. In fact, Morandi made wide use of his own experience in this field as well as of that of other leading designers, in order to achieve what was an important stage in the development of Italian technique.

Thus the hall, the roof of which was to consist, in the normal Italian way, of parallel beams connected to brick slabs by a special system which would have demonstrated the basic architectural idea of the whole work, obtained in this way its own 'physiognomy'.

Always keeping in mind the second, and permanent, use of the building (an educational establishment) Morandi felt that a series of lecture halls could only be inserted into the main structure and at the same time play a part in its structural system without any attendant limitations as to form, if the project were based on a wide, rectangular module.

A study of the illustrations we have chosen will show how this premise was fully realized. In particular, it will be seen how Morandi wanted to ensure that the secondary structures placed around the perimeter of the main roof would not hide the basic structure, but would on the contrary make its nature even clearer from the exterior, and would emphasize his research into form, making use of their own stresses and loads to reduce the high bending moments in the span.

From these few notes it is clear how, here again, Morandi's fundamental concept lies in the search for an expressiveness arising from the clear-cut demonstration of the static function. And this relationship is so clear, and so close, that little need be added to clarify it: the extreme simplicity of the plan, the clarity of the outlines and the neat way in which the building fits into the given space and the existing road system are sufficiently obvious from the illustrations.

It is, on the other hand, worth describing in detail the system of circulation proposed, emphasizing the quality of wholeness of the building, which is plain from the transverse sections. The volume of the halls, the peripheral galleries and the lateral structures on two floors form a true whole, the flexibility of which would have made possible a number of uses, owing to the great elasticity of the internal connections. In fact, using the design with ring galleries all carried either externally or internally, the egress arrangements would give uninterrupted easy access to every part of the building.

This would be particularly important, both while the building was in use for the International Exhibition of Labour and, subsequently, when it would have become the headquarters of the National Centre for Professional Education, and would, in fact, make possible the simultaneous use of the building for this latter purpose and for possible future public exhibitions. This absence of specialization in the plan was obviously something Morandi wanted, its essentially simple and, indeed, almost elementary, nature making possible many different solutions within the various sectors.

From this basis of the work it is plain that the structure would have retained its validity from the point of view of appearance even if the few finishes planned had been reduced to a minimum at the execution stage. In fact, the entire concrete structure would have remained exposed without any facing, using marble for paving only. Indeed, Morandi deliberately avoided introducing roof lights into the roof, as he felt they would be useless in any application of the building, as natural lighting would in any case be insufficient unless the entire roof were to become a vast and costly translucent expanse.

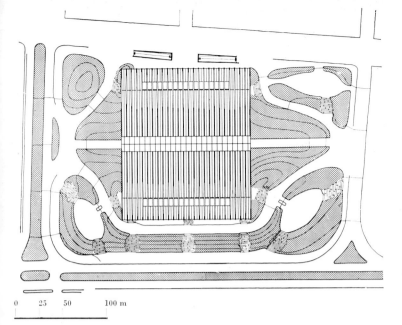

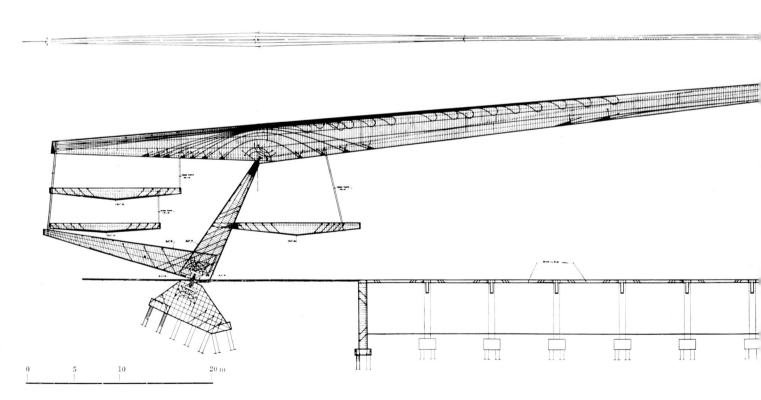

Left: site plan: *below:* plan and section through the reinforcement of one of the prestressed transverse members: *right:* a view of the model

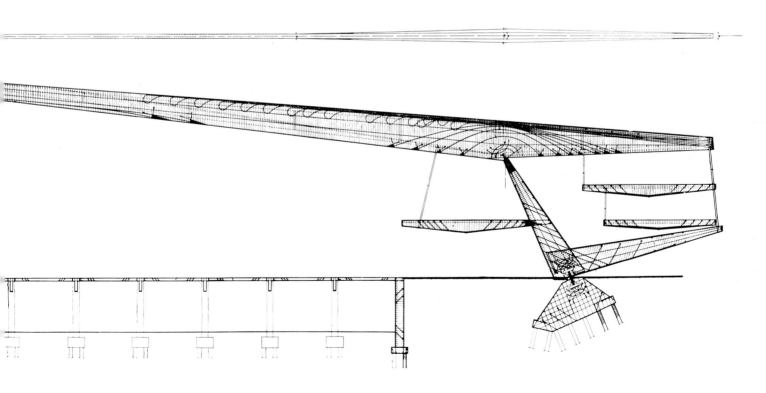

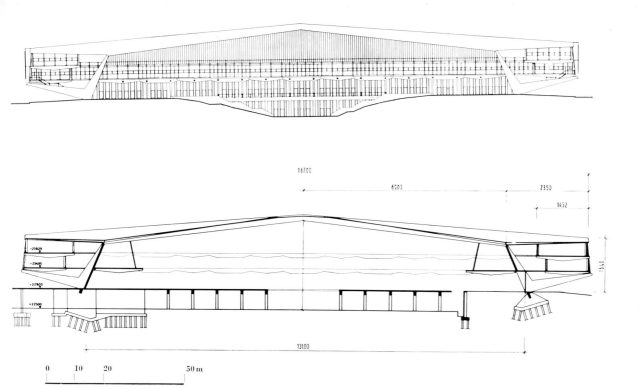

16700

6200   2350

1452

+27829
+27490
+22900
+22300

1340

13100

0   10   20   50 m

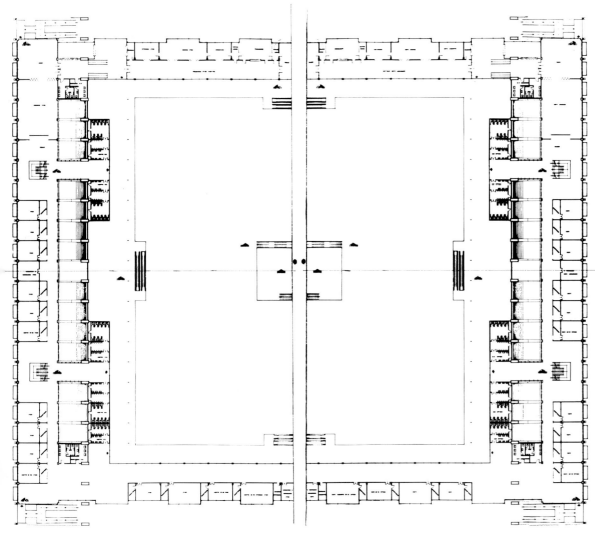

Front elevation, transverse section and pla
of the building on a level with the large per
*pheral galleries: **right:** views of the model*

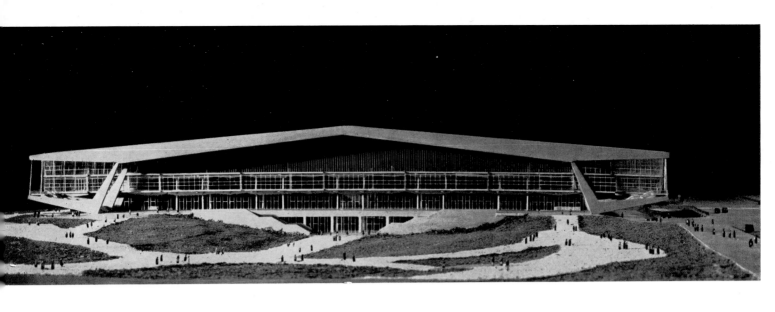

Via Olimpico viaduct, Ro.

The construction of a bridge in a city is always looked upon as an indication of the state of development of the 'Art of Construction'. As in Rome fifty years ago Hennebique's Risorgimento bridge marked the opening of the age of large reinforced concrete city bridges, today, in many cities, works are appearing which are in the van of prestressed concrete technique. Outstanding among them are Morandi's bridges in Rome, Florence and Sulmona, which are illustrated here.

The two Roman bridges (that over the Corso Francia, and the project which was not carried out for a bridge over the Tiber at Tor di Quinto), and that at Sulmona, show three variations on the same theme which, in turn, Riccardo Morandi took up methodically and elaborated with results which really achieve finality.

In these examples he solved the problem of a large span crossing with a special type of prestressed structure which in the last few years has had several applications notable for the elegance of their structural and formal treatment. These enable exceptionally large spans to be crossed with a minimum number of vertical supports.

This structural system consists of a beam resting, at points before the ends, on two raking columns, and continuing beyond them as a cantilever, the ends of which are fixed by high tensile steel ties anchored at the base of the columns. These ties are given a prestress such that the moment induced by them in the span partly compensates for that existing in the simply supported beam.

This interesting application of prestressing has, moreover, made it possible to avoid the use of large piers and arches, and was thus specially valuable at Sulmona because it avoided placing obstructions in the soft ground of the river bed. The known mishaps of a bridge recently constructed in Rome led Morandi to adopt solutions which would produce neither excessive vertical loads nor heavy horizontal pressure on the foundation soil.

The special arrangement of the sections of beam in the length of the span emphasizes the different purposes of the three elements which compose it: the central section, which provides the required clear span, and the two lateral sections which provide the link between the central section and the banks, and which were designed to frame and set off the central section with such lightness that they become a determining factor in the appearance of the work.

The 'stylistic' continuity between the three sections is provided by the side elevations of the beams which, of identical depth, and a colour different from the other parts of the work, form two continuous strips which visually express the depth of a single ideal slab. The special shape of the frames which support the central span is, moreover, an interesting expression of the plastic qualities which are closely allied to the function of each member, and the slightness of the dimensions make each 'pier' seem almost transparent in regard to the span, giving the already slender structure of the beams a semblance of still greater daring.

These works show plainly the material from which they are built. The only concession to special finish is the bush hammering of the whole visible surface, to expose the basalt aggregate used in casting the inner beams, and the limestone used in the outer ones, in such a way as to accentuate the luminosity of the surfaces exposed to the sunlight in relation to those in shadow.

There is no particular difference in concept between the Via Olimpica viaduct (the first of this series of bridges) and the bridge which links the centre of Sulmona with the new 'Piano della Potenza' quarter, crossing the valley of the Vella (the last of the series). The only notable difference, in fact, concerns the length of span to be crossed, and the closer study which has been made of points of detail and of the construction work which is evident at Sulmona and which, as said earlier, marks a positive achievement. This achievement, from many points of view, can really be considered as final in this type of structure.

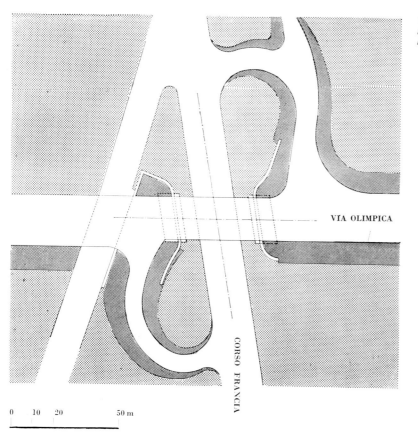

Top: *soffit of the Vella bridge:* **left:** *layout of the viaduct and access links to the Via Olimpica from the Corso Francia:* **right:** *a view of the soffit of the viaduct, showing the fusion of the beams where they approach the supports:* **below:** *plan of the project*

VIA OLIMPICA

CORSO FRANCIA

0 10 20   50 m

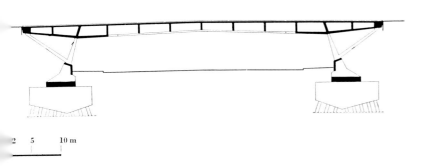

2 5   10 m

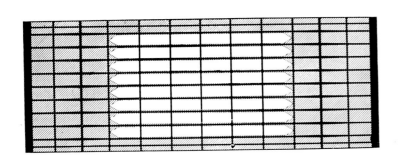

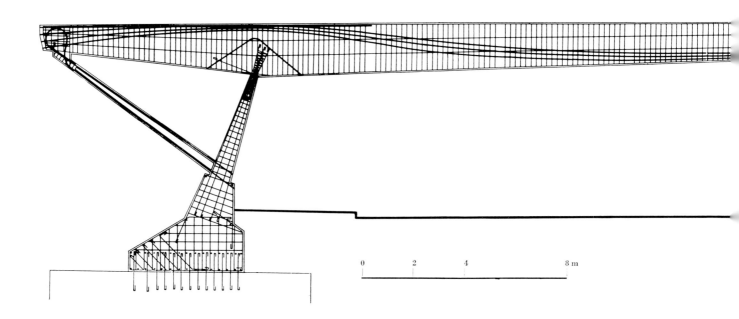

0   2   4   8 m

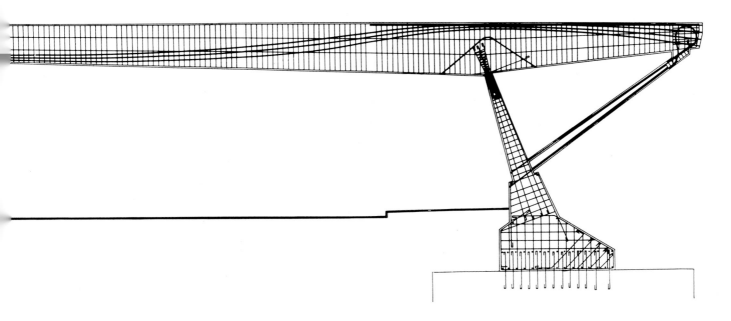

The Via Olimpica viaduct seen from the Corso Francia

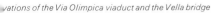

Elevations of the Via Olimpica viaduct and the Vella bridge

5   10   20 m

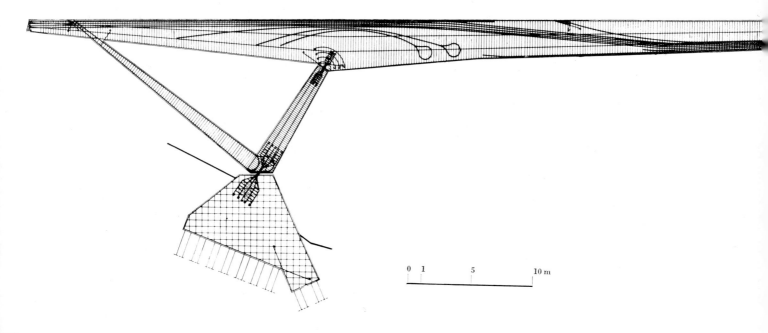

...ering and scaffolding of the Vella bridge, and longitudinal section showing the reinforcement

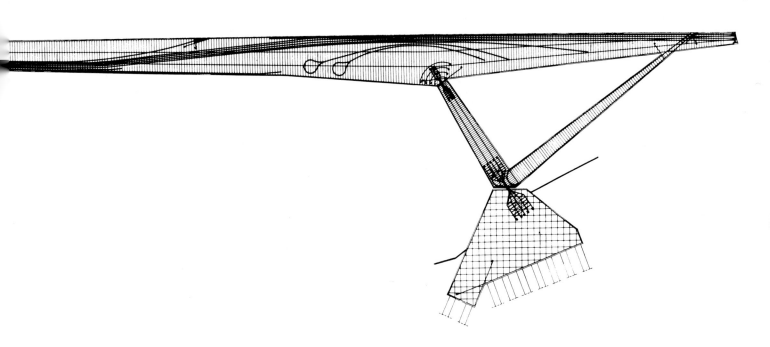

81

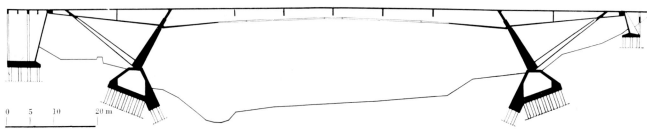

0   5   10   20 m

Vella Bridge

Quercia-Setta viaduct—vertical p

Quercia-Setta viaduct on the Autostrada del Sole
Overpass bridge on the Autostrada della Cisa

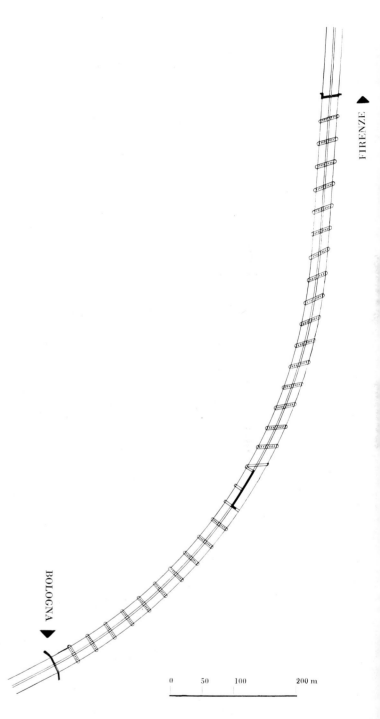

ere we have grouped together two bridges which, though they are
ot actually similar in appearance, nevertheless had to meet similar
equirements, both in use and in construction. We can compare two
ariations on the same theme, which have produced unusually
nteresting results.

hese works were first of all studied having regard to the economic
equirements. In the first, where the problem was to carry a road at a
noderate height above ground level, and on a good foundation,
Morandi used moderate spans. Among other things, he had to take
ccount of the fact that the whole work would be on a curve and
hat long spans would have complicated the problem from the
tructural point of view, because of the torsion in the beams. In the
econd case, in which the central portion of the work had to be at
bout 623 ft. above ground level, he again used straight beams (but
f longer span) ; this was because a series of arches, for example,
would have necessitated the use of steel centering which would
ave meant an enormous amount of very costly construction work.

n both cases, therefore, the solution adopted seemed not only that
which, aesthetically, adhered most closely to the requirements of the
ery long crossing, but which was also the most practical : vertical
upports carry two transverse members which in turn carry the
eams of the central span to be crossed.

ut let us examine, in turn, the differences and the resemblances
etween the two projects.

Plan of the Quercia-Setta viaduct

87

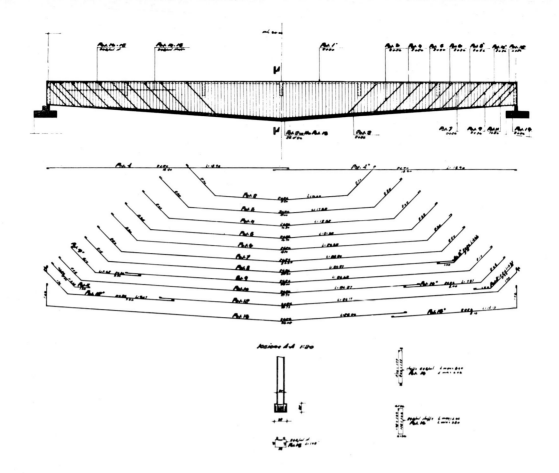

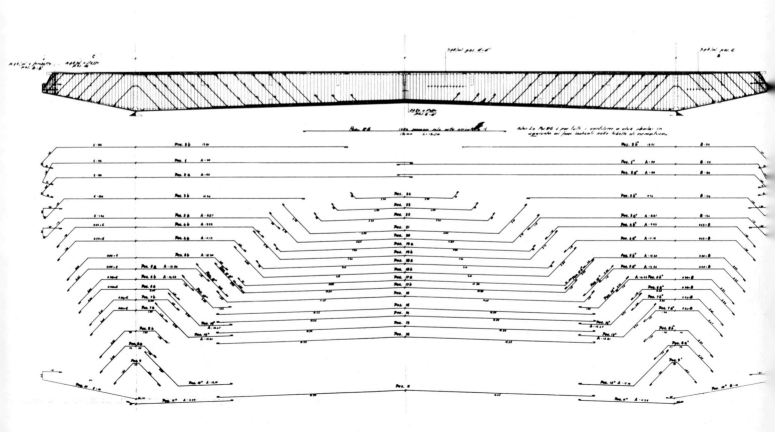

Reinforcement of the suspended beams and the cantilevers, Quercia-Setta viaduct (original working drawings)

Quercia-Setta viaduct. The Quercia-Setta viaduct, altogether over half-a-mile long, crosses in a wide curve the valley of the variable river Setta, which tends to flood at certain seasons. It consists of a series of 'Gerber' beams, all approximately 118 ft. long, carried on vertical piers designed as a series of open members, so that in spite of their size they have a remarkable transparency and subtlety in appearance. These members are cast into a continuous base only in the length of the bridge which forms the actual river crossing, and only to a height corresponding to the maximum possible high water.

This, of course, was not a structural requirement, but rather was Morandi's way of preventing material carried down by the flood from becoming wedged between the slender supporting members and damaging them.

The horizontal members forming the deck are shaped according to the lines of the tensile forces, so as to reduce as far as possible the amount of material used in them (and, hence, its dead weight). This has the effect of enhancing the repetitive rhythm of the piers, in a design which is both genuine and restrained.

As regards economy of construction, it should be said that all the beams which rest on the 'Gerber' joints were precast on the ground and raised into position by a speedy mechanized system of lifting.

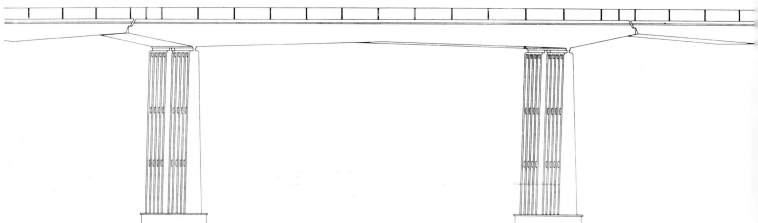

... ction of the intermediate beams, placed on the cantilever ends: they were cast immediately
... ow their final position; *below*: sectional plan of a cantilever beam

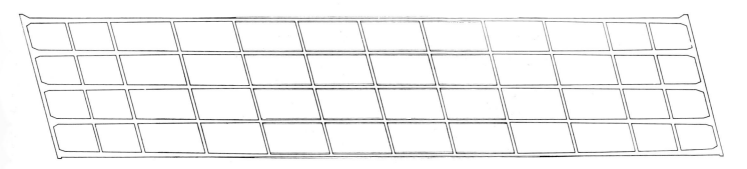

0 1   5   10 m

t: original drawing of one of the two viaducts over the Cisa

duct bridge over the Cisa. The Cisa viaduct bridges were en-aged by Riccardo Morandi as motorway bridges with two super-posed carriageways carried at a considerable height ; they consist a series of tall, hollow columns capped by four pairs of brackets signed to carry, as in the previously described bridge, beams of e required span.

ven the particular technical characteristics of a work of this scale, d bearing in mind the economic requirements laid down at the rt, it will be as well to consider in detail the method of execution olved by Morandi.

e essential feature of the method was the elimination of complex d costly centering. He then had the idea of constructing each llow rectangular-section column section by section in telescopic el forms, so that each section was carried on that previously cast, d in this way the columns could be built at relatively low cost. At out 65 ft. from the height envisaged for the lower deck, two tem-rary 'fans' would have branched off from each pier for the casting the first pair of cantilevered brackets. In this way a great part of e structure could be cast economically, using the columns eady constructed as supports for the remainder.

e connection between the portions of the lower carriageway can-evered from two adjacent columns was effected by 118 ft. long pre-st, prestressed concrete beams cast on the previously constructed ackets, and launched successively from a special travelling girder,

so that temporary staging based on the ground becomes un-necessary.

With the lower carriageway completed in this manner, the upper one was planned for construction in the ordinary manner, with centering supported on the lower during cast. In this way the four cantilevered elements were cast above the previously constructed ones while the top centre span was crossed by 82 ft. prestressed con-crete beams either launched in a similar manner to those of the lower deck, or, in the traditional way, by using temporary staging carried on the completed deck below.

The reason for the different lengths of the pairs of brackets which spring from each pier lies in the fact that, in order to avoid an exces-sive difference in level between the two superimposed carriage-ways, with a consequent increase in the work of levelling between the bridge and the existing road, Morandi reduced the depth of the top beams as much as possible, and so, in order to remain within economic limits, reduced their span as compared with that of the lower deck beams.

Together, however, all these 'dry' reasons have led to great visual expressiveness—a fundamental characteristic of all Morandi's work, in which 'technical and economic requirements always lead to forms of great architectural value, because they are filtered through a highly-developed sensitivity to design'.

97

Elevation and longitudinal section of one of the two Cisa viaducts: *right:* vertical sections throu...
the structure supporting the two superimposed decks

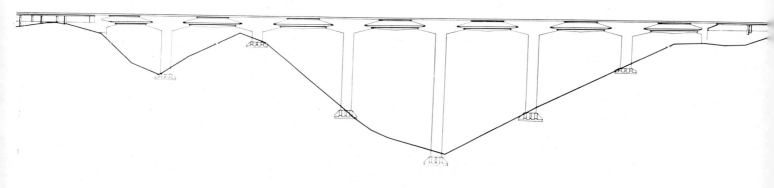

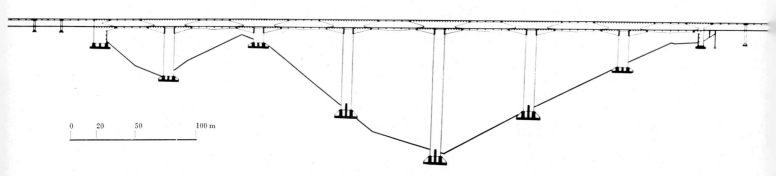

0   20   50   100 m

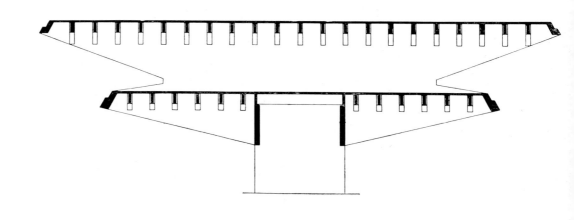

5   10 m

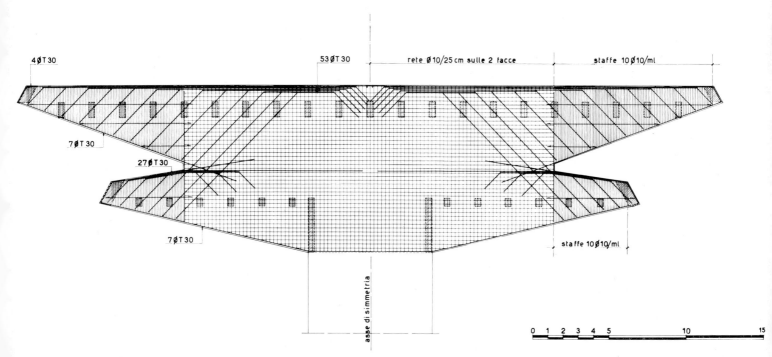

| 4 Ø T 30 | | 53 Ø T 30 | rete Ø 10/25 cm sulle 2 facce | staffe 10 Ø 10/ml |

7 Ø T 30

27 Ø T 30

7 Ø T 30

staffe 10 Ø 10/ml

asse di simmetria

0 1 2 3 4 5   10   15

rete/mesh : sulle 2 facce/on two faces : staffe/stirrups

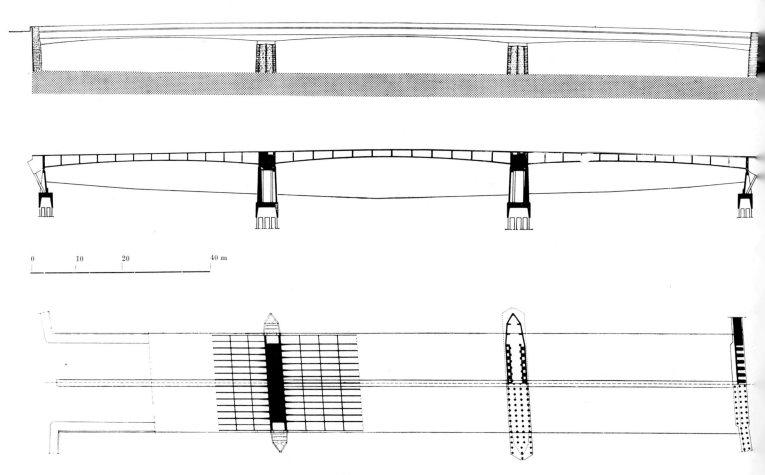

0   10   20   40 m

orandi has rebuilt two bridges in Florence: the San Nicolò and
e 'Amerigo Vespucci'. Both are stylistically very fine, although
ey had to solve very different problems—partly overcome in the
se of the former, very much present in the case of the latter.

ie former, indeed, is of approximately the same dimensions as
ennebique's Risorgimento bridge, and the Foro Italico and
frica bridges, all in Rome. It differs from them in the elimination of
e structural spandrels and in the adoption of a relatively thin arch
parate from the supports, but this difference is not apparent to the
e, as the heavy anti-shock spandrels remain and falsify the archi-
ctural concept.

the second, on the other hand, the delicate problem of inserting
modern structure into a beautiful historic setting (if only on
count of the dangerous proximity of the noted Santa Trinità
idge by Ammannati, rightly considered one of the finest bridges
the Italian Renaissance) was courageously faced. The problem,
oreover, seems to have been satisfactorily solved by Morandi, if
ie reflects that the Florentines themselves—always severe and
ustic critics—have been satisfied with the result—although, in its
iy, that was not the case with the new S.M. Novella railway
ation!

ie horizontality and obvious stability of this bridge, which give it
ch a decisive character, derive directly from the method of conruction chosen for the loadbearing elements. The horizontal mem-
rs consist of three simply supported beams resting on the two
utments and two piers. The central beams, which have a theo-
tical span of 177 ft. 4 in., and the side ones, with a theoretical span

of 164 ft. 8 in., are in prestressed concrete, and, being designed
independently, act as simply supported elements although they are
tied down at their ends by ties contained within the piers and the
abutments. This arrangement has made it possible to achieve a
remarkable effect of lightness, through the shallowness of the
beams—a shallowness imposed by the water levels, and also by the
need to provide a smooth ride-in from the adjoining roads.

The central beams form a cellular structure of the type already seen
in the previous bridge. They consist of two horizontal slabs with a
constant thickness of $4\frac{3}{4}$ in., and thirteen vertical ribs with a constant thickness of 6 in.; only at the abutments and in the small cantilevered section is this last dimension increased from 6 in. to 27 in.

The cellular system is completed by a series of transverse diaphragms designed to give rigidity to the structure in the transverse
direction; a roller bearing supports it at one of the abutments; the
seatings consist of suitably profiled steel plates; at one end the
system is tied together by a series of hinges formed by round steel
bars.

The side spans are similar in construction to the central one, but
have twelve longitudinal ribs. The shape and arrangement of the
abutment ties were also, as will be seen in the drawings, modified in
view of the different static and technical conditions at these
supports.

The entire bridge structure is in bush-hammered concrete, with the
piers and abutments clad externally with blocks of 'Serena' stone—
that essentially Florentine stone.

101

One of the two concrete commemorative plaques at the ends of the bri
(design by Liugi Gori)

Part longitudinal section at the central piers, showing the line of the prestressing cables

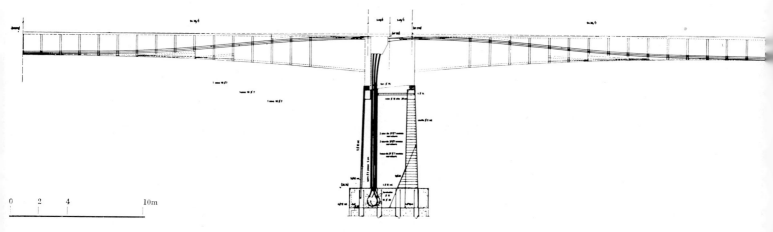

0   2   4   10m

102

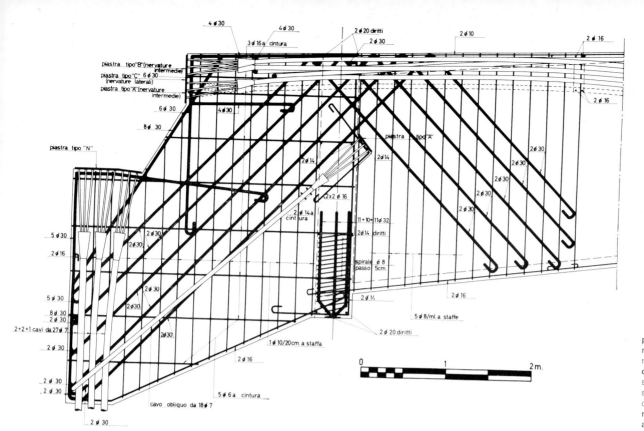

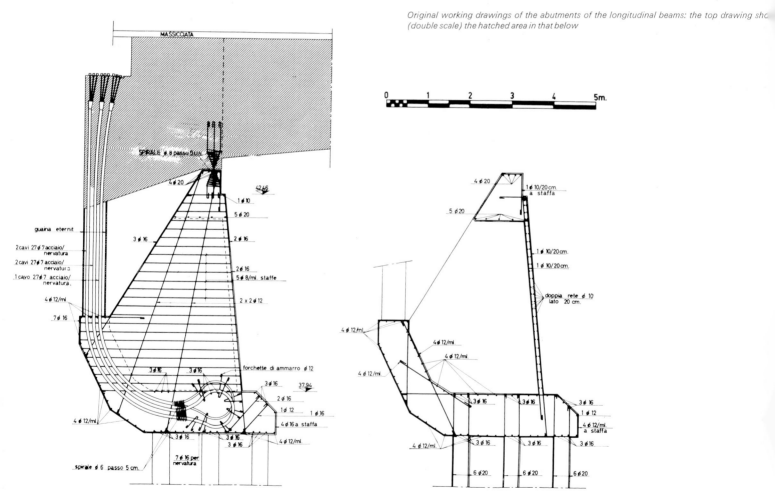

piastra tipo 'B' (nervature intermedie)/ plate type B (intermediate ribs): laterali/side: cintura/band: diritti/straight: spirale/spiral: passo/ screw pitch: cavi/cables: staffe/ stirrups: guaina eternit/asbestos cement sheath: acciaio/steel nervatura/ribbing: forchette di ammarro/anchorage forks: doppia rete/double mesh

Original working drawings of the abutments of the longitudinal beams: the top drawing shows (double scale) the hatched area in that below

S.T.T. power station at Civitavecchia
Santa Barbara power station at Castelnuovo dei Sabbioni
A.B.C.D. works at Ragusa, Sicily
S.E.N.N. nuclear power station at Garigliano
SELT-Valdarno thermo-electric power station at Leghorn

Here we have grouped together five versions of a frankly modern subject, to which Riccardo Morandi has given high aesthetic quality, expressing through architectural form the human value of man's achievements in the industrial field.

Civitavecchia power station. The most characteristic feature of the first power station mentioned—that at Civitavecchia—is the coal-loading bay, which includes a very long enclosed conveyor belt carried on an inclined gantry. The loading bay and the coal crushing plant are at the lower end of this gantry, while midway along its length is the exchange tower for unloading crushed coal.

The forms of the loading bay and the tower were conditioned by the unusual shape and slope of the huge inclined gantry, and the gantry-tower-loading bay group therefore takes on the appearance of a highly original architectural concept.

The loading bay, prolonged as a 52 ft. long cantilevered canopy, was designed by Morandi as an individual structure, hinged to the underground members. The exchange tower was also treated as a hyperstatic system.

The tower for the discharge of crushed coal at the Civitavecchia power station

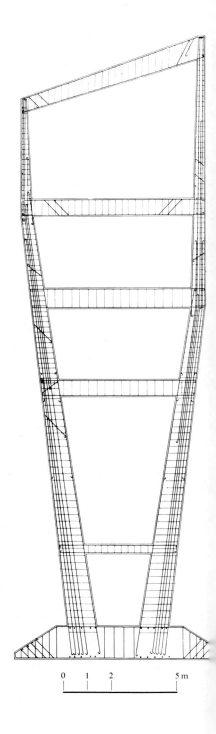

0   1   2   5 m

coal loading and crushing base: *below:* longitudinal section and sectional plan of the
opy

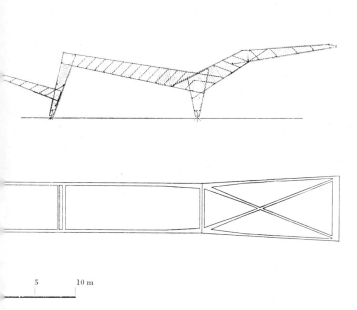

5   10 m

Cooling towers and conveyor belt at the Santa Barbara power sta

Santa Barbara power station at Castelnuovo dei Sabbioni. The Santa Barbara power station was designed for a production of about 340,000 kW. It was the first power station to be designed entirely by Riccardo Morandi, and one of the largest now in production in Italy.

The site plan shows the layout of the main and secondary buildings, the transformer station and the auxiliary structures. Among these will be noted the two thin reinforced concrete cooling towers (6 in. thickness) which are 262 ft. high, two 328 ft. high reinforced concrete chimneys at the base of which are the electrostatic filters for the collection of fly ash, the water purification plant, the chemical laboratory, the pumping station for fuel oil and for feeding the boiler-house, the porter's lodge, cloakrooms and lavatories, silos for ash and lignite, the conveyor belt with its housing, the workshops and stores—all grouped organically around the main power station structure.

All these buildings, the design of which was the outcome of a careful study of the functional requirements of the different parts of the plant, were arranged on plan after a detailed examination of the problem of circulation within the scheme.

The framed structure of the buildings is exposed to view, both internally and externally, while the infilling walls are faced with glass mosaic to ensure a high degree of resistance to the fumes and lignite dust.

3 No.16 DIA. ANCHORED
TO REINFORCING BARS
OF THE 3RD JOIST

10.00

1∮8/10cm
STAFFE

1∮14

2∮14

3∮14+
3∮16

3∮16

5∮8/ml.
STAFFE

2∮12

1∮8/10cm
STAFFE

1∮24
CERNERA

ST.5∮8/ml.
1∮8/10cm
STAFFE

1∮8/10 cm
STAFFE

8.84

1∮24 CERNERA
2∮10

1∮24 CERN.R4

2∮10

1∮24 CERNERA

GIUNTO
SALDATURA DI
FORZA

2∮12

1∮8/10cm.
STAFFE

5∮8/ml.
STAFFE

2∮10

1∮8/10 cm
STAFFE

1∮12

1∮8/10 cm
STAFFE

2∮10+1∮12

2∮10

5∮8/ml.
STAFFE

1∮8/10cm
STAFFE

2∮10.

1∮24
CERNERA
2∮10+1∮12

1∮12

6.70

0   1   2   2,5m.

116

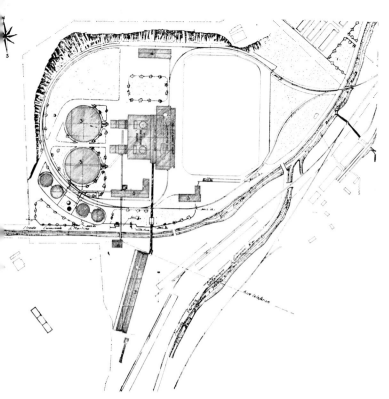

117

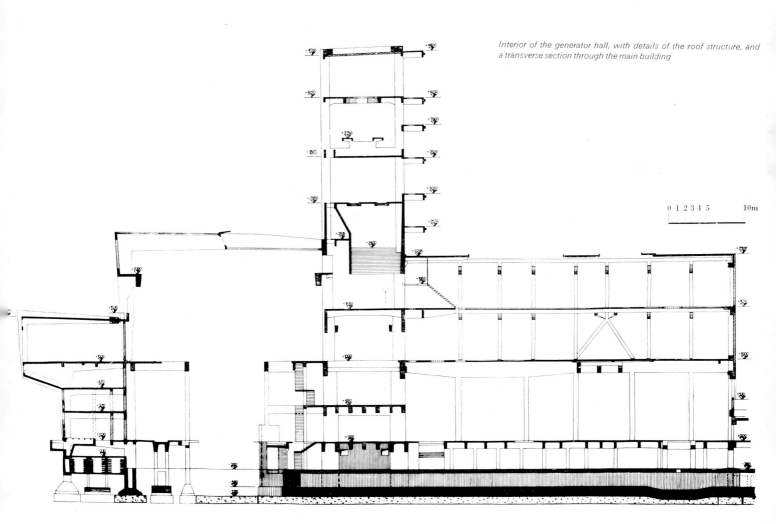

Interior of the generator hall, with details of the roof structure, and
a transverse section through the main building

0 1 2 3 4 5   10m

A.B.C.D. works at Ragusa, Sicily. At this point we would like to include among the power stations a factory at Ragusa that manufactures polyethylene, because it displays so well the results of the technical and aesthetic research begun by Morandi with the factories built at Colleferro immediately after the World War, and pursued by him in the different power stations he carried out. This factory owed its layout essentially to precasting requirements imposed by the site—and which had to provide for a wide variety of shapes and sizes in the buildings making up the scheme. However, while these requirements were a not easily superable obstacle to producing a homogeneous whole, they did not prevent the achievement of some notable results by methods simplified to the utmost.

All the buildings are in reinforced concrete, and in order to achieve maximum lightness in the main loadbearing structure, Morandi adopted the most advanced methods of calculation, while yet keeping the structure within the canons governing work of the highest quality. Simple frames and grids solve the problem of the extensive production areas and *brise-soleil* louvres of undoubted sculptural effect protect the interiors from the dazzling sunlight of southern Sicily.

*erior of the Linde building of the Ragusa works: **below:** perspective of the group of buildings*

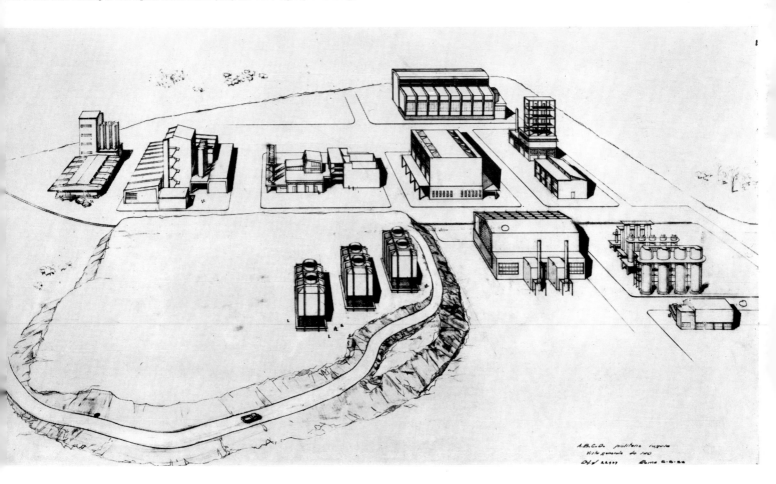

Facade, side view and section of the Linde building: the method adopted for dealing with strong winds on the lateral infilling wall should be noted

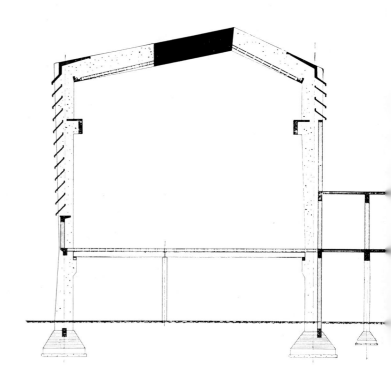

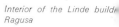

*Interior of the Linde build
Ragusa*

E.N.N. nuclear power station at Garigliano. The designs of arigliano nuclear power station was a special problem, though lated to the previous ones. This work, which is approaching com- etion, is one of the two large power stations of this type now der construction in Italy. It is obviously the reactor which pre- nts the main problem in this highly novel type of industrial build- g. In this instance it is mounted in a steel sphere with a diameter of 4 ft., which makes the best container for any radio-active gas hich might escape in case of accident during working. It also rms an original architectural element which gives a definite aracter to the whole scheme.

side the reactor sphere stands the generator station itself, which uses all the equipment for the production of electricity. This ilding consists of two main sections—one which is the actual machinery hall, and the other which contains the services and controls.

While this second section is similar to conventional thermo-electric power stations, the machinery hall is something absolutely different. Externally it appears as a completely closed concrete volume—the absence of openings being a safety measure against radio-activity.

Any lack of character in such an enclosed and unbroken structure was, however, obviated by Morandi by exposing the frame extern- ally, which imparts an interesting rhythm to the surface. In fact, he approached the whole theme with the intention of emphasizing this quality and making the structure look what it really is—a large, closed concrete container, set off by the large, closed metal reactor container alongside.

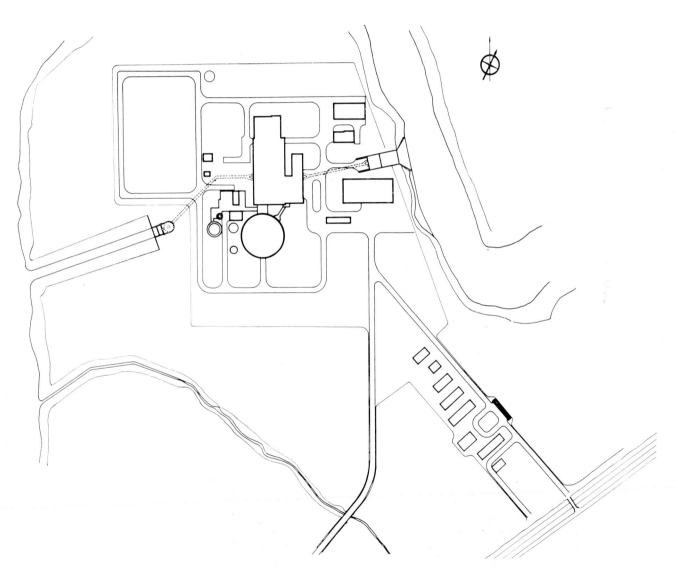

1—Reactor   2—Generating station.   3—Store

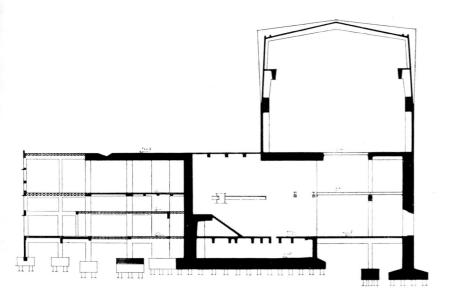

Transverse and longitudinal sections of the large generator

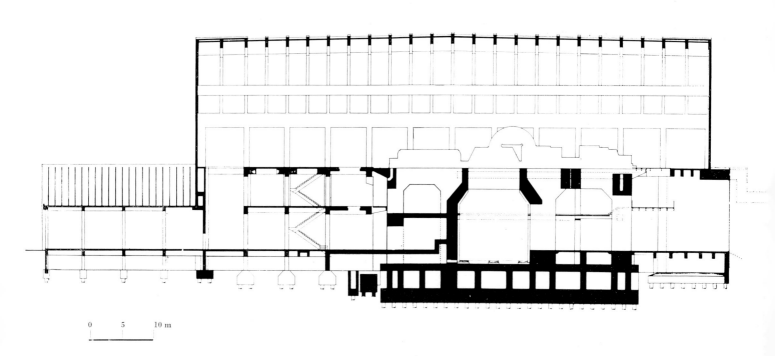

0   5   10 m

133

The Leghorn power station seen from the

SELT-Valdarno thermo-electric power station at Leghorn. This power station, the most recent of Morandi's designs in this field, is situated near Leghorn, and is based on the sole and continuous use of sea water for cooling purposes. It includes two groups of generators of 152 and 155 mW, and consists of two reinforced concrete chimneys 197 ft. high, at the base of which is laid out the equipment for the electrostatic filters and the smoke extractor fans, a building for the purification of water, with chemical laboratory attached, buildings for the extraction of sea water, the porter's lodge, cloakrooms and washrooms, workshops and stores, and a building for the Diesel oil pumps, in addition to the power station itself. This last has a total volume of about 210,000 cu. yd.

This building contains the boilers, which are carried on a steel frame supported by a reinforced concrete structure at level plus 17 ft. 6 in.; the eight-storey building designed to service the boilers, and the three-storey coal silos, the last of which, 46 ft. high, is roofed with prestressed concrete beams (prestressed on the Morandi system) with a clear span of 82 ft.; and the control buildings containing the transformers, the electrical control rooms and the offices.

All the buildings are arranged on plan after careful research to ensure the most functional layout.

Highly complex problems of statics, arising from the heavy loads and the vibration of the machinery, had to be solved in the construc- of this power station.

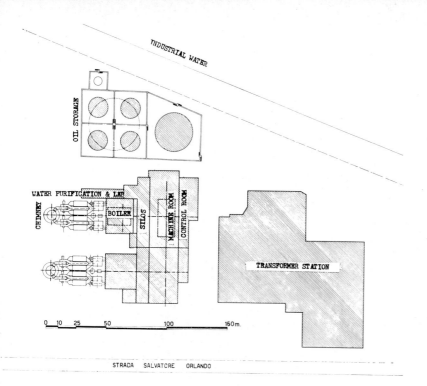

INDUSTRIAL WATER

OIL STORAGE

WATER PURIFICATION & LAB

CHIMNEY

BOILER

SILOS

MACHINE ROOM

CONTROL ROOM

TRANSFORMER STATION

0 10 25   50   100   150 m.

STRADA   SALVATORE   ORLANDO

left: plan of the Leghorn power station
below: longitudinal section

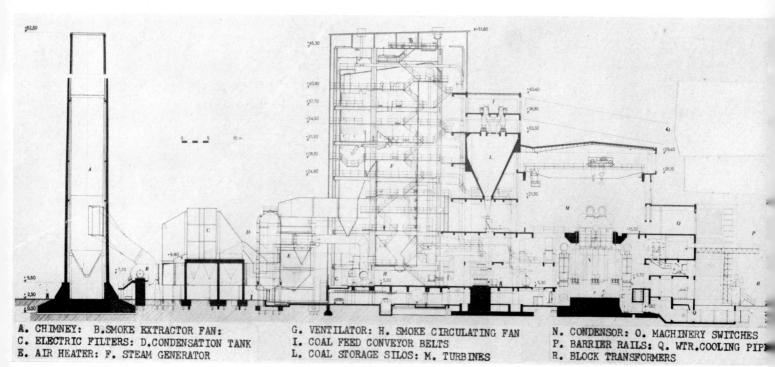

A. CHIMNEY: B.SMOKE EXTRACTOR FAN:
C. ELECTRIC FILTERS: D.CONDENSATION TANK
E. AIR HEATER: F. STEAM GENERATOR

G. VENTILATOR: H. SMOKE CIRCULATING FAN
I. COAL FEED CONVEYOR BELTS
L. COAL STORAGE SILOS: M. TURBINES

N. CONDENSOR: O. MACHINERY SWITCHES
P. BARRIER RAILS: Q. WTR.COOLING PIP
R. BLOCK TRANSFORMERS

Equipment for placing the ties of the large central trestles of the Maracaibo brid

Bridges over the river Tartaro at Canda, near Udine (project)
Bridge over Lake Maracaibo, Venezuela
Viaduct-bridge carrying the Genoa-Savona motorway over the Polcevera Valley

At this point it seems to us worth while pausing a moment to consider a particular solution recently developed and carried out by Morandi for spanning large distances : huge triangular, lattice-like trestles with the tensile forces inverted and the load acting directly on a horizontal element carried by inclined members acting as ties. Before starting on the work Morandi made a long and careful study of this type of 'balanced-element' bridge, in collaboration with the Turin, Zurich and Stuttgart Polytechnics, and the Model Testing Institutes at Bergamo and Lisbon.

Bridge over the River Tartaro. Our first example, which has not yet been carried out, is a project for one of the bridges over the Tartaro at Udine, for which Morandi proposed a statically determinate structure of two equal spans. In it the central support, instead of being a pier common to both spans, consists of a pair of prestressed cables acting as ties which, after passing over the top of a trestle structure, then passes down into a reinforced concrete box filled with rubble. Each cable is housed in a concrete sheath which contains the separate wires, leaving them free to move within it.

After the concrete is cast, the cables are re-tensioned to prestress the sheath, so that in use it remains permanently in compression and the extension of the cables under loads passing over the deck only brings about a diminution of the state of compression, in such a way as to prevent cracking. The structure is thus resolved into two independent sections, one of which is supported at the ends (on one of the abutments, and on the cantilever end of the other) and the other hinged to the abutment at one end and suspended at midspan from the system of cables the ends of which are buried in a massive, reinforced concrete, transverse member.

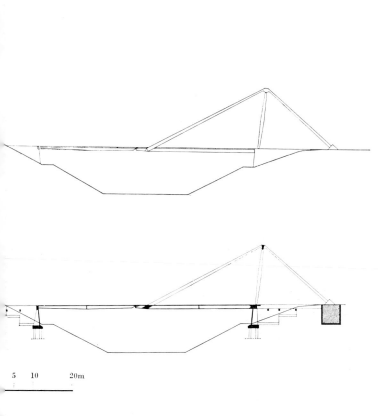

5   10   20m

ation and longitudinal section of one of the Canda bridges

143

Bridge over Lake Maracaibo, Venezuela. Of far greater importance, both from the point of view of size, and the result obtained is, however, the second of our examples—the bridge over Lake Maracaibo. Here, the use of balanced elements is so integral to the structure that it becomes a genuine architectural problem.

The real difficulties of carrying a motor road over the lake did not all lie in the length of the structure (about $5\frac{1}{2}$ miles), or the foundations, or the junctions with the existing and future road network, but rather in the need for shipping to be able to pass under the structure without limitation of size or time, and it was this requirement which made the project one of the most demanding ever to have been tackled by Morandi.

Lake Maracaibo will, in fact, carry constant, interweaving streams of shipping to and from one of the greatest petroleum-producing centres in the world, together with the traffic of an important port, now under construction, which will be the outlet to the whole of northern Venezuela and Colombia. The bridge, moreover, will link the city of Maracaibo, with a population of over 600,000, with the famous Pan-American Highway which runs the whole length of the continent.

The navigable channel through the lake is off-centre, and over this area the bridge had to provide a clear opening 1,312 ft. wide and 164 ft. high, with a further five spans of 492 ft. length and 164 ft. height on either side. The remainder of the viaduct, joining the main spans to the shore, could be designed as desired.

From the point of view of execution, it seemed at first sight as though the main portions of the bridge should be constructed in

steel, and this was the view taken by the different competitors w submitted designs in the international competition organiz Morandi, however, considered that the tropical conditions, co bined with the salinity of the atmosphere, would be extrem damaging to ferrous metal and would have meant the expendit of huge sums on subsequent maintenance. He, therefore, submit a design entirely in concrete as being the best and most suita material for the work.

For the central span, under which passes the greater part of shipping, he decided to use a structural form similar to that at Ud as this enabled him to use elements which, though fairly cumb some, were nevertheless relatively light, with a negligible thickn of beam carrying the deck. In the smaller spans, on the other ha he remained faithful to the pattern, by now almost traditional v him, of grouped-column piers, bringing them, however, into ha ony with the dominant trestle-frames of the main spans.

We will now examine section by section the various parts of bridge, which in the final version was considerably altered from originally submitted design. The stretch comprising the 771 ft. sp (the major part of the bridge) consists of six long adjacent gird which together form a single continuous box beam with six c phragms. The four inner ones are governed by four inclined st intersecting diagonally, and the two outer ones by the tens members which pass over an A-shaped reinforced concrete tre frame which is structurally independent of the inclined s structure. The girders are of cellular construction, and are stressed in part by steel cables and in part by the compres generated by the horizontal component of the forces of

144

sion members. These latter are in their turn tensioned by the
ad weight of the connecting beams supported on the end of the
x girders.

particularly interesting form of structure is that used for the trans-
rse members which anchor the cables to the beams, and whose
action is to provide for the uniform distribution of the forces over
e whole width of the deck. Considerable shear stress is generated
the deck and to counteract this it was necessary to prestress with
reat number of heavily curved prestressing cables.

tween the ends of the two balanced cantilever beam systems are
spended four parallel prestressed concrete beams with a span of
proximately 150 ft., which rest on the former through ordinary
ker bearings; this arrangement is similar to that used in the other
dges described.

randi designed these balanced systems to be completely inde-
ndent from one another so that in the case of possible uneven
tlement of the foundations no unforeseen stresses would be
used, which could be particularly dangerous in a structural system
this scale.

e horizontal deck structure rests at one end on fixed supports and
the other on rocker bearings. It consists of a system of four con-
uous ribs with the soffit forming beams of uniform strength
ied by a top slab and also by two transverse beam members at
supports and three others in the length of the span.

e next spans down in size—those of 279 ft.—are divided by
uped-column piers, each formed of four inclined slab-shaped

columns of varying heights, joined together at mid-height and at
the top by transverse members. They are so placed that their shape
and slope is the same for all the spans, in spite of the varying level of
the road. These slab-columns carry a similar number of prestressed
concrete beams, which tie the pairs of inclined members together
and cantilever approximately 131 ft. beyond them; the 150 ft. span
beams described above are carried on the end of these beams.

The precasting yard for the beams and piers set up on the shore of
the lake deserves particular mention. We also felt it would be of
interest to include some photographs of this, from which some idea
of its scale and its importance to the work of construction can be
gained. It, in fact, made possible, among other things, the placing
of nearly all the horizontal members without centering. In the
stretch at the Punto Iguano end, for example, which comprises all
the smaller spans, which vary in height above water level, pairs of
ribs cast on the ground were launched simultaneously by means of
suitably-designed floats, half the width of the road deck being
satisfactorily carried out in each operation. The four ribs forming the
deck were precast separately, assembled in pairs on the floats, and
then transported by water to their position between the piers; at this
point, the floats placed the pairs of beams on the supports, partially
submerging them. The whole operation of loading, transporting and
launching of each pair of beams took on average only two hours.

A similar method of construction and launching was adopted for the
150-ft. beams, with the sole difference that, in view of the height of
the supports, it was necessary to use a number of tower cranes to
raise the level of the floats to that finally required. For the casting of
the tower trestle frames, on the other hand, a special steel grid form
of centering was used, placed on 164 ft. high steel supports.

145

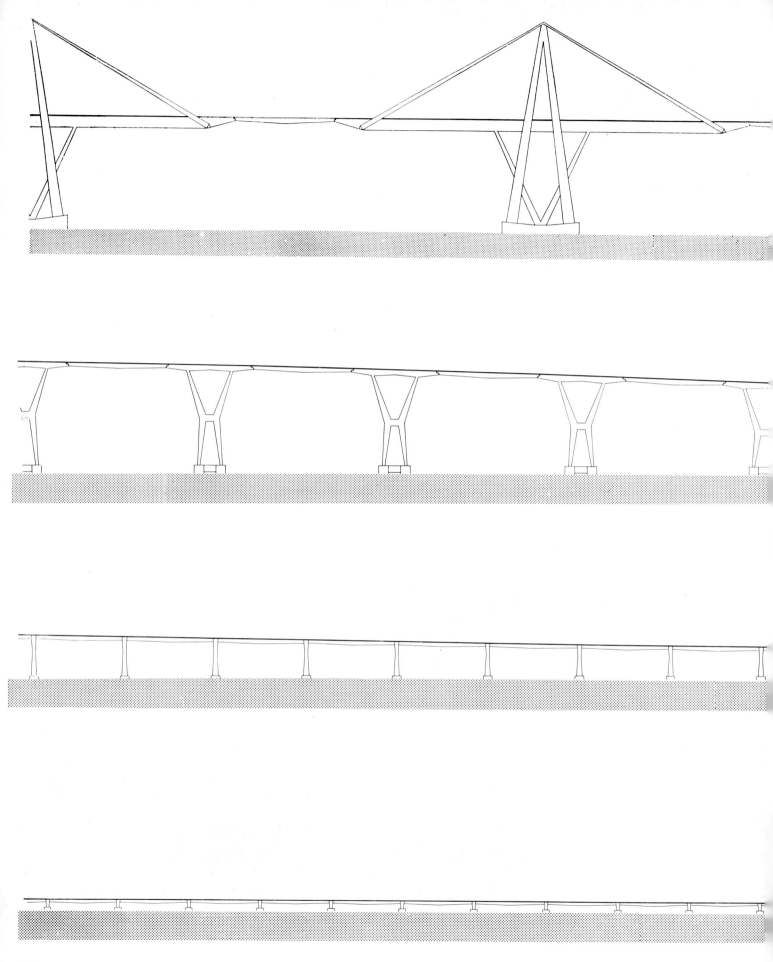

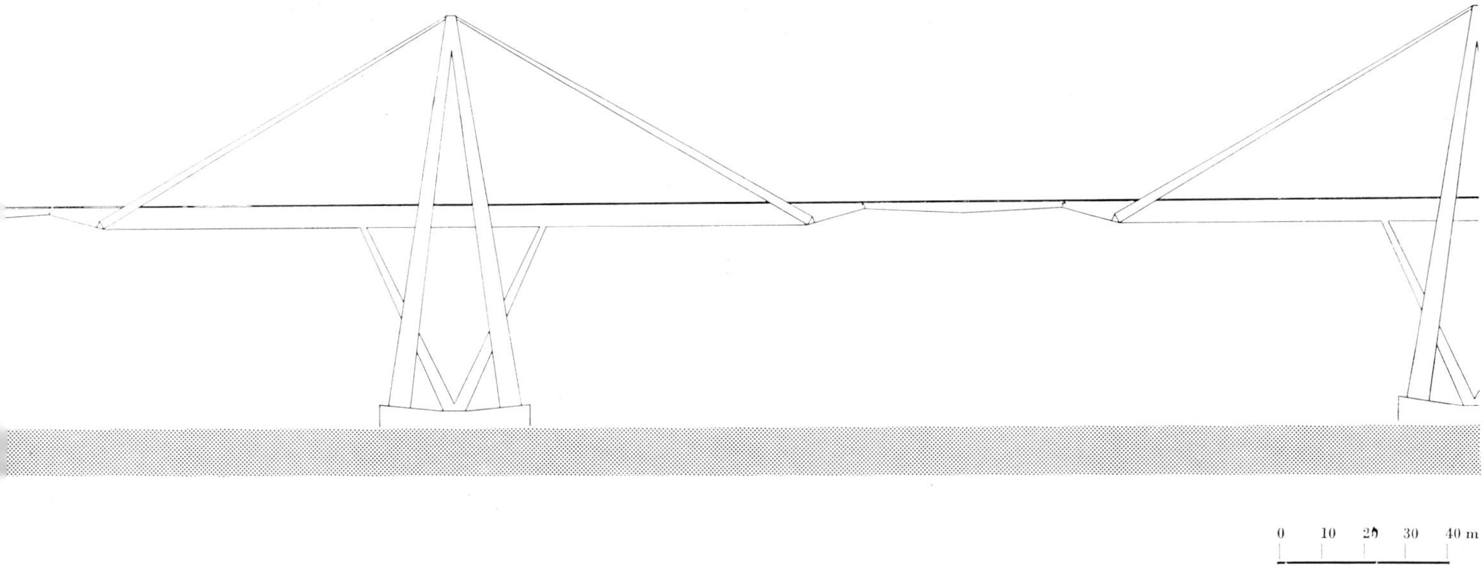

vation of different parts of the Maracaibo bridge. ***Reading from top downwards:*** *the 771 ft. span 279 ft. span: the 150 ft span and the 120 ft. span*

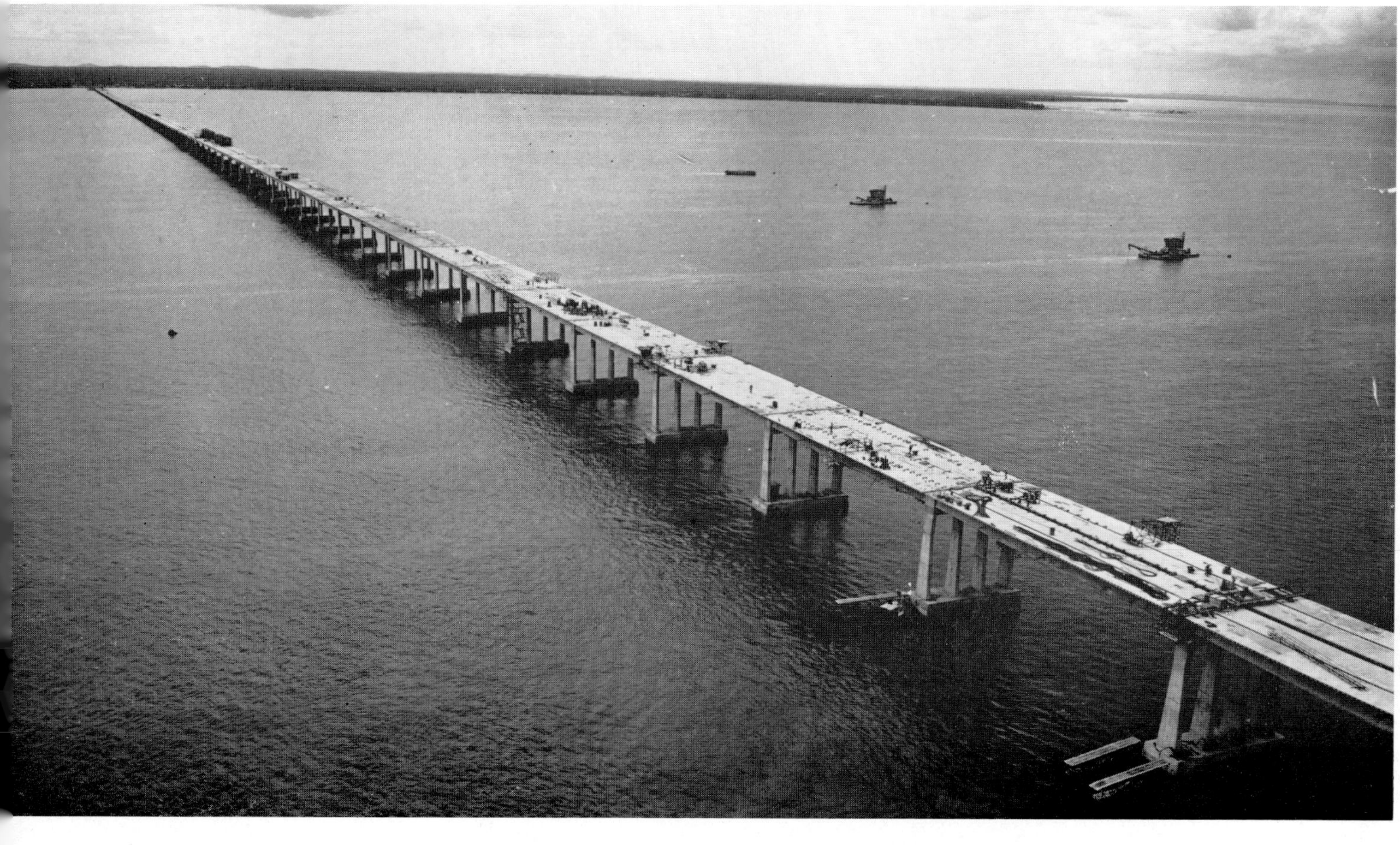

ws of the casting yard for Maracaibo bridge. **Top:** the area used for the foundation
s; **in the same picture, bottom left:** the piles completed and ready for transport to
site, and, **centre right:** the circle where the outer casings are cast. **Bottom left:** the
area and also that for the beams. **Bottom right:** the stock of launching beams and
loading dock. In the background can be seen the work-people's village, and be-
d, the town of Maracaibo

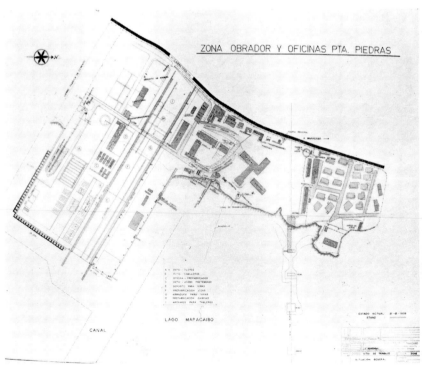

Right: view and original plan of the casting yard

On pages 150 and 151; stages in the manufacture of the foundation piles in a separate casting yard; beginning to cast one of the 'vacuum concrete' outer casings which form the loadbearing element of the piles; the ducts for the prestressing cables can be seen: driving a 197 ft. pile entirely cast on land, within a steel casing used to bore into the sea bed: the head of a section of pile, completed and filled with in situ concrete, with radial grooves to form the connection with the best section: each pile is in fact made up of six segments joined together and prestressed on land before being transported to the site: transport of a section of pile: loading test on the piles of a pier, at water level, by means of a floating crane

152

Views of the sites at sea where the lateral trestles are cast

The centering and re
forcement of a cantile
being lifted and tra
ported from the cast
yard to the site in
open sea

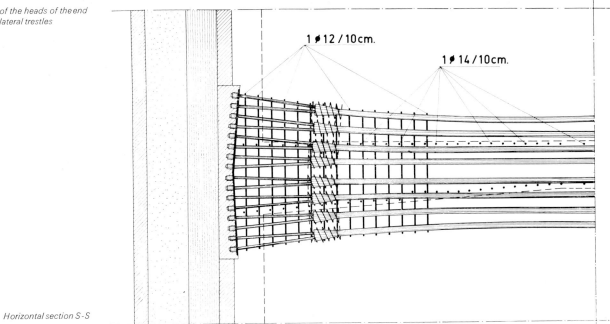

1 ⌀ 12 / 10 cm.

1 ⌀ 14 / 10 cm.

Horizontal section S-S

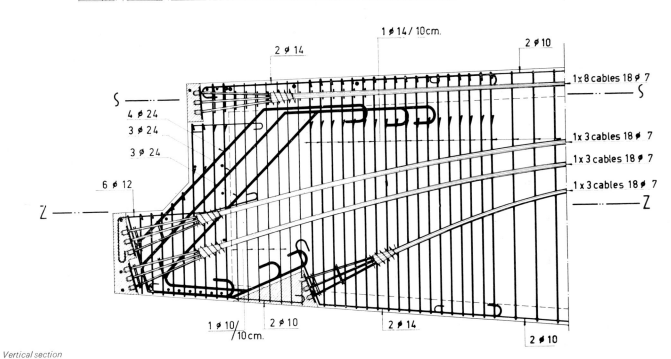

1 ⌀ 14 / 10 cm.

2 ⌀ 14

2 ⌀ 10

S ——— S

1 x 8 cables 18 ⌀ 7

4 ⌀ 24

3 ⌀ 24

3 ⌀ 24

1 x 3 cables 18 ⌀ 7

1 x 3 cables 18 ⌀ 7

6 ⌀ 12

1 x 3 cables 18 ⌀ 7

Z —·—·— Z

1 ⌀ 10/ 10 cm.

2 ⌀ 10

2 ⌀ 14

2 ⌀ 10

Vertical section

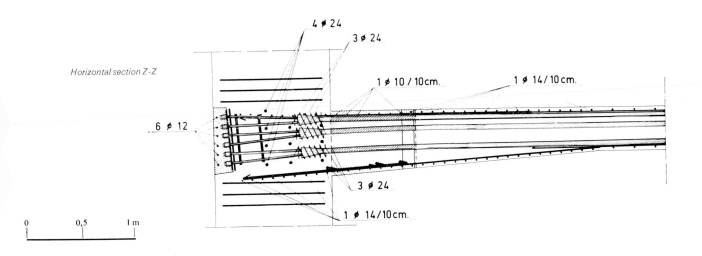

Horizontal section Z-Z

4 ⌀ 24

3 ⌀ 24

1 ⌀ 10 / 10 cm.

1 ⌀ 14 / 10 cm.

6 ⌀ 12

3 ⌀ 24

1 ⌀ 14/10 cm.

0   0,5   1 m

155

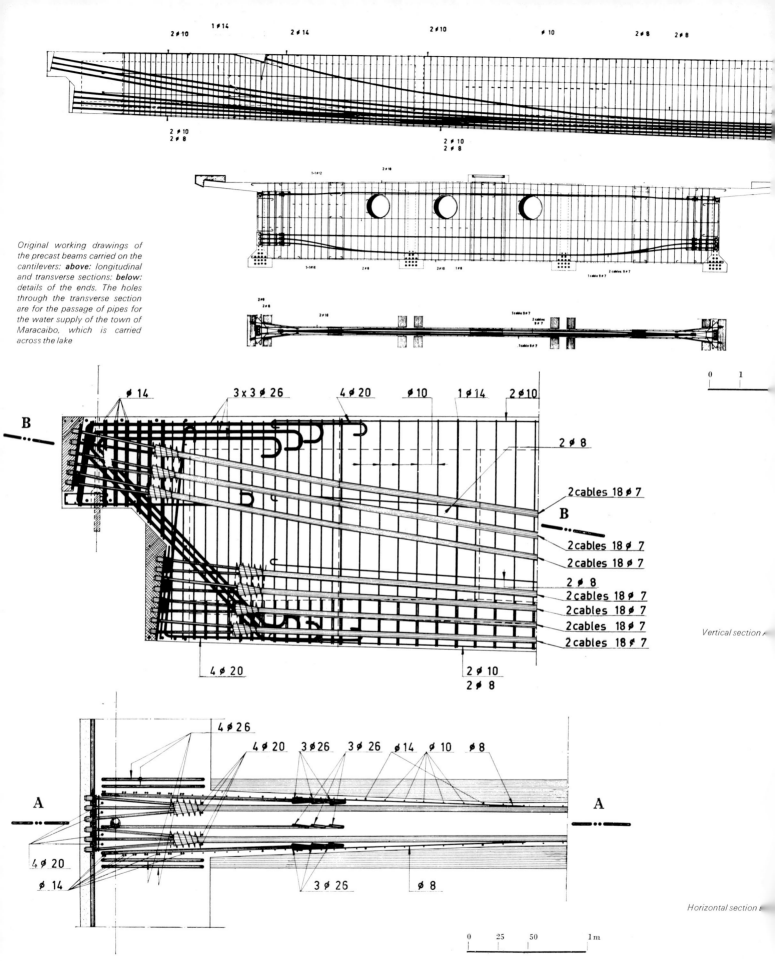

*Original working drawings of the precast beams carried on the cantilevers: **above**: longitudinal and transverse sections: **below**: details of the ends. The holes through the transverse section are for the passage of pipes for the water supply of the town of Maracaibo, which is carried across the lake*

2 ⌀ 10   1 ⌀ 14   2 ⌀ 14   2 ⌀ 10   ⌀ 10   2 ⌀ 8   2 ⌀ 8

2 ⌀ 10
2 ⌀ 8   2 ⌀ 10
                              2 ⌀ 8

⌀ 14   3 × 3 ⌀ 26   4 ⌀ 20   ⌀ 10   1 ⌀ 14   2 ⌀ 10

B

2 ⌀ 8

2 cables 18 ⌀ 7

B

2 cables 18 ⌀ 7
2 cables 18 ⌀ 7
2 ⌀ 8
2 cables 18 ⌀ 7
2 cables 18 ⌀ 7
2 cables 18 ⌀ 7
2 cables 18 ⌀ 7

Vertical section

4 ⌀ 20   2 ⌀ 10
                          2 ⌀ 8

4 ⌀ 26

4 ⌀ 20   3 ⌀ 26   3 ⌀ 26   ⌀ 14   ⌀ 10   ⌀ 8

A   A

4 ⌀ 20
⌀ 14

3 ⌀ 26   ⌀ 8

Horizontal section

0   25   50   1 m

sing the reinforcement of a beam prior to placing it in the formwork

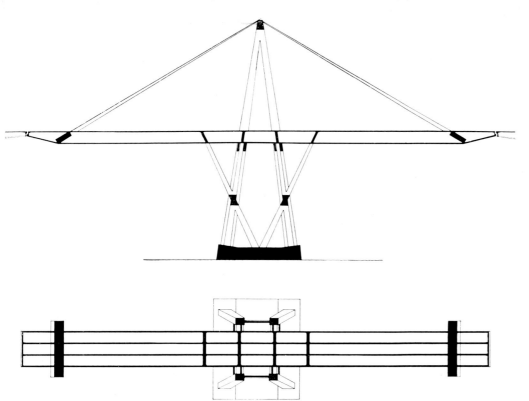

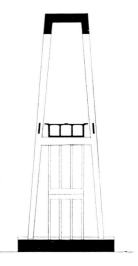

Vertical and horizontal sections through one of the la central trestles

0 10 20   50 m

Stages in the construction of the central trestles, and the p ing of the central steel centering, prefabricated on the sh for the casting of the side beams: the temporary vertical s ports which carry the centering are more than 164 ft. high.

160

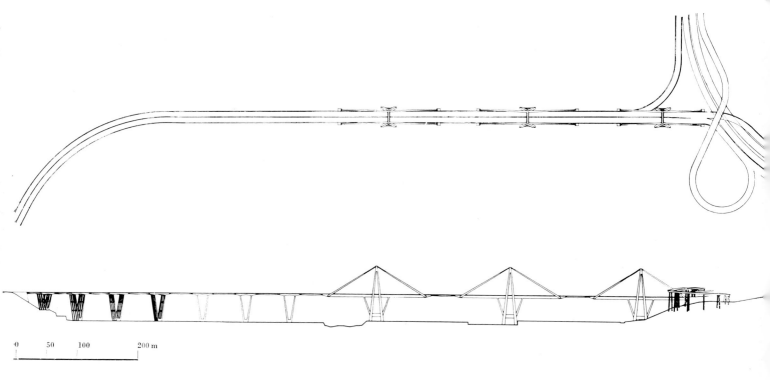

0 50 100   200 m

168

Viaduct-bridge over the Polcevera. Similar in every way to Maracaibo bridge, but more demanding from the architectural point of view owing to its special surroundings, was the project for the viaduct-bridge over the Polcevera and the road link between it and the Genoa-Po Valley-Savona commercial traffic trunk road. As will be seen from the illustrations, the viaduct falls into two distinct parts: one which crosses the Campasso railway yard, the Piazza d'Armi railway yard, and the Polcevera river valley, and one which passes over a residential district. These different requirements enabled two quite different structural systems to be used: special reinforced concrete balanced cantilever tower trestle frames for the first, and the familiar grouped-column supports for the second.

This viaduct, which is over a kilometre long and at a level of plus 56.20, has dual carriageways each 24 ft. 6 in. wide, with a central reservation and footpaths; it consists of a number of different spans, the longest of which is 689 ft. From these data, which closely resemble those of the Maracaibo bridge, and from the fact that it occurs in an urban setting, it is clear that it will be a highly interesting structure, both from the technical and architectural points of view. In particular, the spans which pass over the two railway yards, and which are of unusual length for a flat reinforced concrete bridge, provide opportunities for a valuable study of form and planning in relation to an existing city setting.

On the basis of successful past experience, Morandi, here again—for the same reasons of space, and cost, which obtained in Venezuela—designed large trestle frames with beams partly supported on them and partly suspended by prestressed cables passing over the tops of the inclined masts at a height of 138 ft. 6 in. above the carriageway.

By prestressing the cables and the reinforced concrete sheathes enclosing them it was possible here not only to reduce the asymmetrical loads, but also that due to variations in temperature. The effect of this becomes negligible even in the longest spans, whereas it would have been quite prohibitive had any other static design been used.

By launching the beams it will be possible to construct the large spans over the railway yards without scaffolding, and the whole process of construction will be carried out in such a way that the railway traffic will not suffer the slightest interruption.

All the viaducts linking with the existing road system will be carried on cantilevered reinforced concrete beams built into the piers and made integral with a deck slab 5 in. thick by means of 6 ft. deep ribs and suitably placed transverse elements. The whole system will rest on dual supports, carried on the rock foundation through large foundation blocks. The design of approach ramp is conventional.

Model of connecting road and one of the ends of the viad

A general view of the Göteborg bridge (original draw

174

Bridge over the port of Göteborg (project)
Bridge over the Scheldt at Antwerp (project)

These projects, drawn up for two international competitions held in 1963, show alternative schemes for bridges over a port, the structure of which, with a prestressed concrete deck and outstanding architectural qualities, creates a world record for size. They form a happy conclusion to a long experience in reinforced concrete 'trestle' structures, which, as already pointed out, have considerable advantages over other now classic designs, as they eliminate any maintenance costs (since all the steel used is covered by concrete), and form a highly efficient system.

The structure, similar to that previously illustrated, is based essentially on the most appropriate use of the materials (steel and reinforced concrete) so as to keep all the compressive stresses within the concrete beams and all the tensile stresses within the steel suspension cables.

The basic concept of such a structural system has successfully passed the experimental stage, since the last tests carried out on the Maracaibo bridge and the Polcevera viaduct. The experience gained in the construction of these bridges, in fact, confirmed the technical and economic value of a structural design of this type.

Göteborg bridge. The Göteborg bridge has a total length of 2,711 ft., a total width of 93 ft. and an area of 265,870 sq. ft.
The main piers, which limit the centre span, are 1,368 ft. apart, and are placed so as to comply strictly with the requirement of the competition, that there should be easy access to the dock basin for large shipping.

Starting from the main piers and proceeding towards the south bank, there comes next a span of 410 ft., and at its end, the anchorage block of the suspension cables of the beams. Continuing southwards comes, next, a continuous beam over five spans, one of 59 ft., three of 41 ft. and one of 31 ft. which ends on the southern bank: the lengths of these spans are determined by the line of the approach roads.

Moving northwards and starting from the main piers of the centre span, there comes a span of 410 ft., which ends at the anchorage block, and two spans, still of the same length, which terminate on the northern bank.

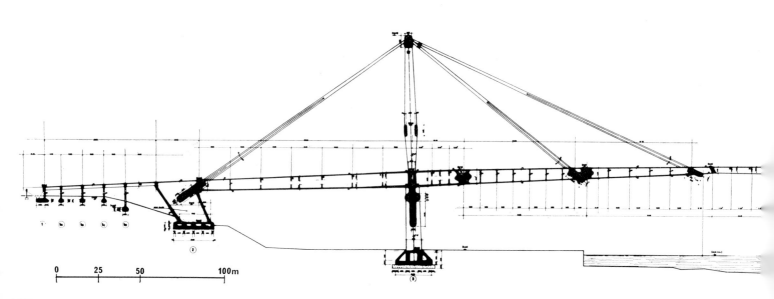

0   25   50   100m

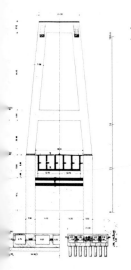

above: a view of the riverside
below: longitudinal and transverse sections through a trestle

177

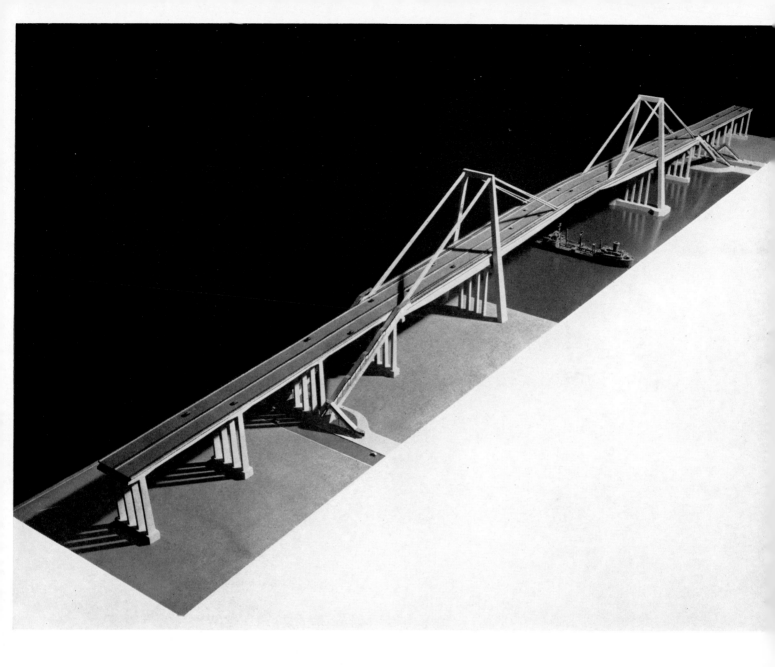

model of the Antwerp br

Project for the bridge over the Scheldt at Antwerp. The bridge at Antwerp forms the principal crossing of the Scheldt. Together with its approach ramp, it is situated near the main points of entry of the road system of the region and of all the main urban road links.

This design, like the preceding one, is very light and, by emphasizing the broad lines of the surrounding countryside, conveys an essential feeling of grandeur, obtained by a study of form and structure, without any indulgence in purely decorative detail. It would, moreover, have made a real contribution to the character of the surrounding country, with its definitely horizontal lines.

The whole project consists of four main sections: the bridge over the river itself, the main links on the two banks, the secondary links on the two banks, and the auxiliary civil engineering works of lesser importance.

The structure contained between the centres of the main piers has a total length of 2,017 ft. 9 in.; the total carriageway is 301,390 sq. ft. The main pier nearest the right bank of the river has its centre 82 ft. from the river bank, so that the clear width allows of some movement to take place on the water even through this span.

The next pier rises 1,165 ft. away, leaving a clear passage for shipping of 1,041 ft. 6 in. Moving towards the opposite bank, there then comes another pier 426 ft. 6 in. away, and then another 270 ft. away. The same arrangement applies starting from the left bank.

The deck level varies from 187 ft. to about 211 ft. 6 in. The arrangement of the piers leaves clear space for the free movement of shipping, since, with the deck at the levels given above, the dimensions of the supporting structures are such as to permit navigation of the Scheldt over a channel 1,041 ft. 6 in. wide, and with a clearance varying between a minimum of 164 ft. and a maximum of 186 ft. 6 in., between the soffit of the bridge and level 23 ft. (the level of the river banks).

Turning to the roadway, this, together with the centre strip, has a total width of from 100 ft. to 133 ft.

The two outermost ways, designed for cyclists and pedestrians, have a total width of 15 ft. 6 in.; the pedestrian portion is 10 in. higher than that for cyclists.

The traffic on these ways is diverted beyond the trestles and channelled by escalators which carry it to the level of the surrounding roads: this method was evolved so as to enable cyclists and pedestrians to take their place as easily as possible in both the present and future traffic system. In particular, it is worth noting that both the footpath and the cycle track are one-way. All the escalators are designed for the convenient transport of pedestrians, bicycles and light motorcycles.

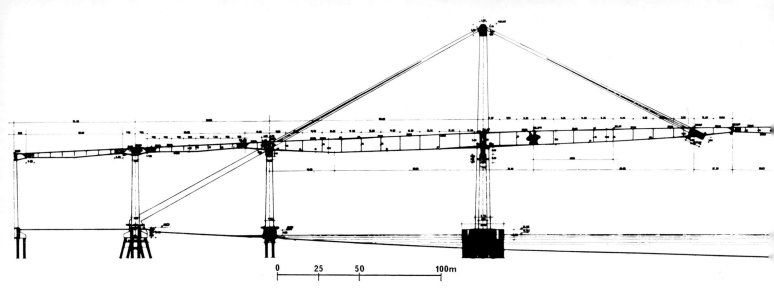

180

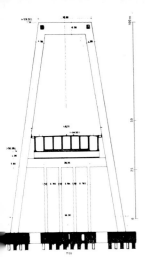

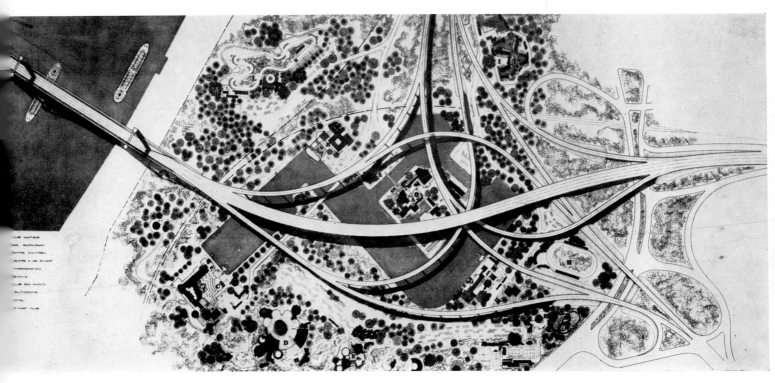

idge over the Escaut at Antwerp.
ove: longitudinal and transverse sections through a trestle
low left: view of the movable access stairs
low right: plan of the road links between the approach and the
rrounding area on the right bank of the Escaut

A. Marine club. B. Bar restaurant. C. Cultural centre. D. Covered theatre. E. Kindergarten. F. Tennis. G. Sports club. H. Velodrome. I. Motel. L. Go-cart club.

181

The model seen from above of the Alitalia hang

Alitalia hangars at the Leonardo da Vinci international airport, Fiumicino

The imposing scheme for Fiumicino airport was designed and carried out by stages, and by a number of designers. Among these Morandi unquestionably takes his place in the first rank, by reason of his authoritative projects and the complexity of the problems he dealt with. These include the access bridge to the concourse, the hangars for Alitalia and the huge terminal building. They were all subjects that he studied very deeply and designed with his customary vigour—although this is not now always obvious, as the original design has in many places been altered on the site by occasional co-operation with other Roman designers at the construction stage.

This is why we have chosen to describe here the hangars of the Alitalia fleet, which Morandi was able to design according to his own deep-felt architectural principles, rather than the terminal building (which won the competition for the design-tender but was subsequently radically altered and underwent many vicissitudes during construction), or the access bridge to the airport (which was to some extent mutilated and made disconnected by the immediate requirements of the moment).

This group of buildings, at the centre of the airport, covers area of about $12\frac{1}{2}$ acres. It provides for two vast hangars, each with a floor area of 183,000 sq. ft., for housing the company's big 'planes, together with a repair shop and a four-storey office block. The buildings which contain the hangars each measure 656 ft. by 279 ft. on plan, and are divided into a vast hall 656 ft. long and 197 ft. wide with no internal supports, and a subsidiary two-storey section of the same length and 82 ft. wide.

These brief details of the required dimensions of the scheme will give an idea of the structural and functional problems which Morandi had to solve. First, and architecturally characteristic, was that of the roof of the actual hangars, since besides an absence of internal supports, there could, in fact, be no external wall to act as a support on the runway side, owing to the need to provide a continuous opening for the possible simultaneous entry and exit of the large intercontinental machines. Thus, the whole of this side had to consist of huge doors, with independent uprights, moving in grooves at the base and fixed at the top to a rail carried on a steel-lattice girder which plays no part in the roof structure.

The roof of the hangars, therefore, and that of the subsidiary section to the rear, are joined together to form a single structural unit, fixed only to the longitudinal wall between the hall and the rear section—a wall which had to be entirely solid (constituting as it does the fire barrier which is obligatory in this building) and which was thus extremely valuable from the structural point of view. The roof consists of a series of curved beams shaped like giant scythes, supported on the fire wall, cantilevered for their whole length over the hangar (197 ft.) and tied at the other end to the rear wall of the subsidiary building which is thereby placed in a state of tension.

These beams are suspended by a system of high tensile steel cables, anchored to tall trestle frames, and after erection, encased in pre-stressed concrete for protection.

As will be seen this is a fresh and exciting application of the prin ciple used at Maracaibo, the full boldness of which, however, will i this case not be appreciated with the completion of the work, owin to the need for a wall to act as a strong crash barrier to the sides c the great halls. On the other hand, the rich texture of the network c cables above the roof still remain visible, and will indicate th suspended roof structure of great scythe beams, and the conse quent self-stressing induced in them by their dead weight.

According to Morandi's usual practice, the whole roof was preca on the ground and raised into position.

As regards the other structural elements of the work, we need on mention the workshop roof—a northlight structure—which carried on a series of specially designed, two-pinned frames wit inclined column members in prestressed concrete. The office bloc presents no particular technical interest.

The highly original solution to the problem of the hangars, whic has the fundamental characteristic of being equally applicable t steel construction techniques as to reinforced or prestressed cor crete techniques, but is essentially an application of precastin techniques, is enough in itself to make of this group of buildings a outstanding scheme. This scheme, though unconventional, takes valid place, architecturally, within a highly specialized tradition th; has produced in Italy itself some of the earliest and finest works c aeronautical architecture.

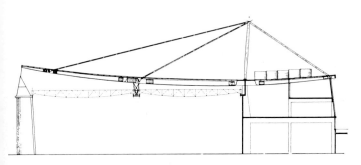

Transverse and longitudinal sections through the Alitalia hangar; the structural independence the sliding doors should be noted, and also the positioning of the upper cables in relation to internal gantry crane

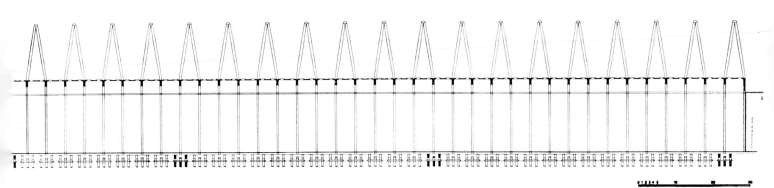

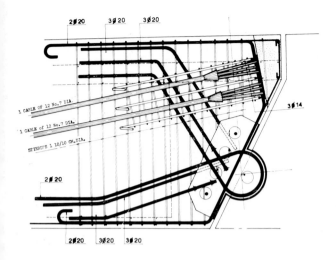

1 CABLE OF 12 No.7 DIA.

1 CABLE of 12 No.7 DIA.

STIRRUPS 1 10/10 CM. DIA.

SEZIONE D-D

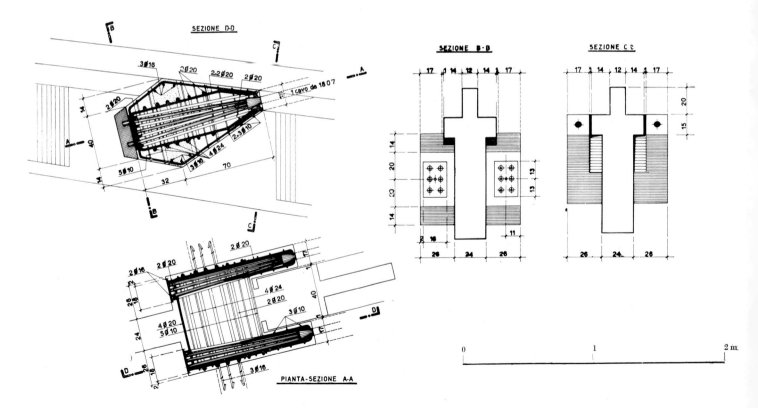

PIANTA-SEZIONE A-A

SEZIONE B-B

SEZIONE C-C

0   1   2 m

186

A hangar seen from one end during construction

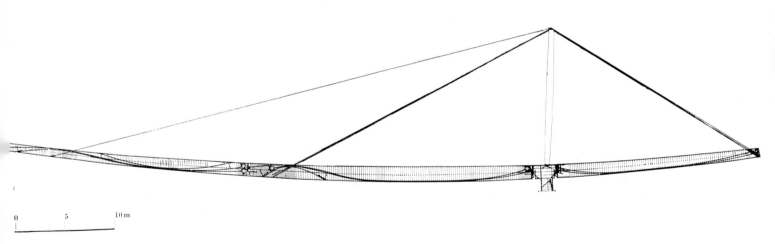

0   5   10 m

gitudinal section showing the curved beams: **opposite: top**—anchorage detail: **below:** detail
wing the attachment of the prestressed ties

Olympic stadium for the Sports City, Teheran (project)

This stadium, the commencement of work on which awaits the consent of the Iranian authorities, is of the type known as 'mixed Olympic'. It provides for football, running, light athletics, etc., and will have accommodation for 110,000 spectators. The arrangement of the seating, which, as in other notable examples, is designed partly with one bank of seats rising above and sheltering another, enables about twenty per cent of the spectators to be under cover.

The arrangement and fixing of the vertical members carrying the banks of seats was designed to provide complete structural unity, and to allow for repetition throughout the whole work, both as regards the superstructure, and those parts which are buried in the embankment foundation. Apart from the circulation areas, the scheme thus appears as a single structural whole, without any discrepancy in style between its various component parts.

The horizontal elements which link the vertical supports make a notable contribution to the architectural quality of the scheme. Here the conventional stairs to the upper seats are replaced by tiers of helicoidal ramps on a gentle gradient; by this means about half the seats can be reached without climbing stairs. The complex of members which carry the large banks of seats, linked by the continuous—and superimposed—slopes of the ramps, form together an outstanding composition which in spite of its rich articulation makes an integral whole which is remarkably light in appearance—this air of lightness is helped by the complete visual separation of the upper bank of seats from the lower.

All the auxiliary accommodation and services for the athletes and staff (including gymnasia, swimming pools, etc.) are grouped in the area below the lower seats, in a series of rooms and halls which are partly buried to the rear. The swimming pools, in particular, are of Olympia dimensions, but will only be used for training by the athletes: the general scheme for the Teheran sports centre provides full competition-standard pools for swimming events.

On completion of the work the entire structure of the above-ground section will be visible, and apparently suspended above the small artificial hill which forms its base and which will be planted with grass and flowers. Light and air will thus enter freely in the area below the upper bank of seats, giving the scheme an air of lightness unusual in this type of structure.

The work is designed in reinforced concrete, with the parts which are subject to the greatest stresses in prestressed concrete. At the design stage complete standardization of the various members has also been envisaged, in order to make it possible to precast the entire work.

del of the structure of the Teheran stadium; the upper tiers seen from below

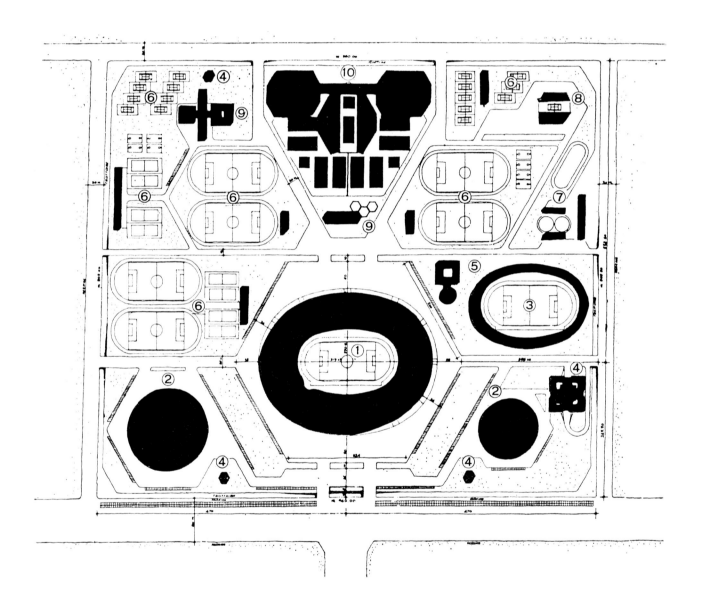

Site plan of the Sports City, Teheran; 1—Stadium for 100,000 spectators: 2—Sports buildings: 3—Stadium for 10,000 spectators: 4—Athletes' accommodation: 5—First aid centre: 6—Playing fields: 7—Horse shows: 8—Tennis: 9—Physical training: 10—Swimming pools and stands

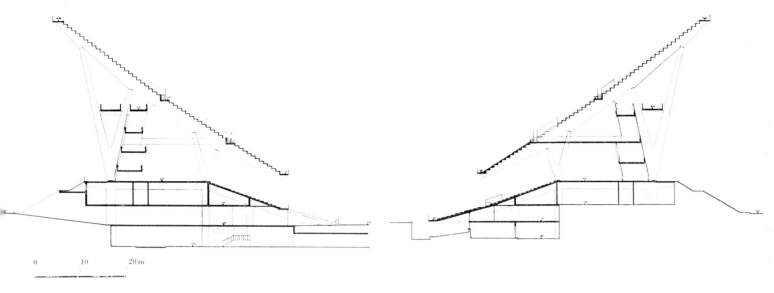

0   10   20 m

Transverse section through the stadium for 100,000 spectators, and plan at level 413,10 (1,359 feet): the use of the space below the lower tiers and the access ramps to the upper tiers should be noted

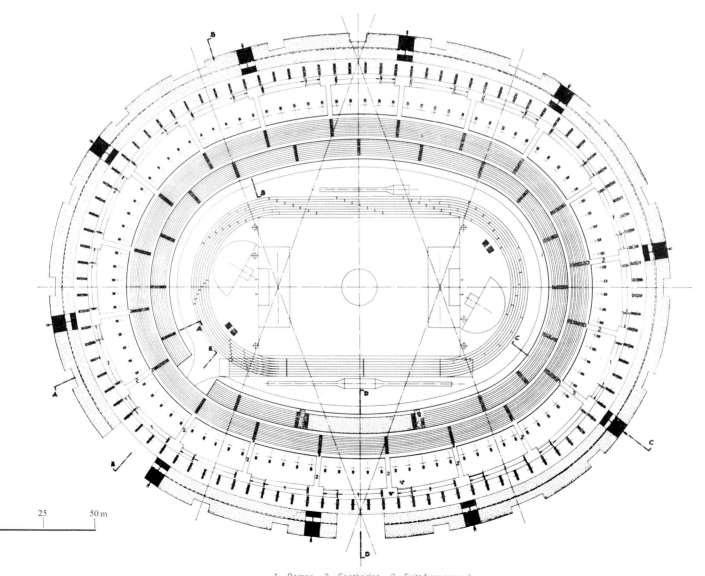

25   50 m

1—Ramps.   2—Footbridge.   3—Exits from ground.

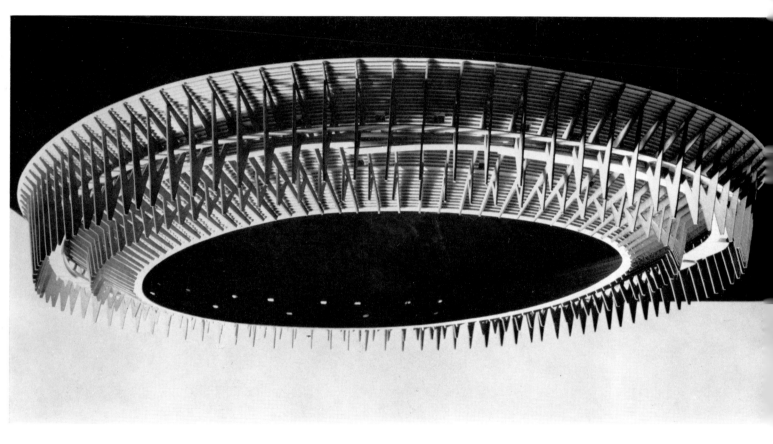

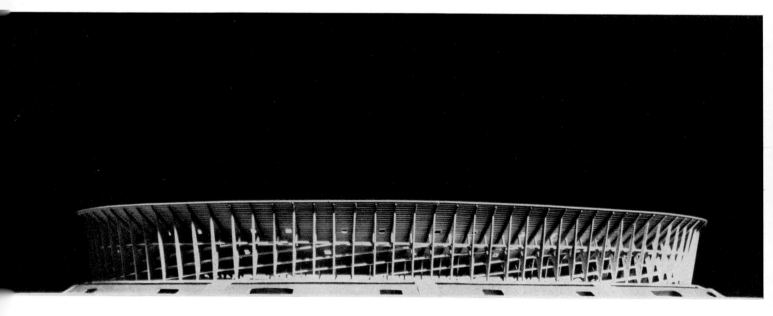

Model of the Piezometric reservoir, R

concluding this brief selection of Riccardo Morandi's work and projects, we should like to include two really unusual projects which, strangely enough, were not favourably received, in spite of the special care with which the functional problems involved were solved, and the aesthetic excellence of the result.

the design of water towers, subject as these are to rigorous functional and economic restrictions, it is not usual to pay great attention to the question of architectural form, and old-established patterns are generally followed, even if they are all too often only moderately suitable, and even clumsy. Such a course is, however, both serious and irresponsible, in view of the way these structures stand out in the urban scene. Good architectural treatment becomes a matter of prime importance.

is, of course, quite true that, generally speaking, the architectural and town planning aspects of the structures present serious difficulties. A very large object has to be fitted into a setting which, in general, is in no sense designed to take it. A 'shape' has to be developed and built, which, while ensuring the absolute functional efficiency of the structure, not only does not upset the balance of the surrounding landscape but actually adds something positive to . The designer should, therefore, create a work which is meant to be looked at' and not merely 'put up with'—a work which needs no concealment or excuse, but which will have its own justification and its own individuality, while clearly and unashamedly announcing its function.

thinking on precisely these lines, and making quite plain his declared intention not to succumb to the temptation to use traditional or customary solutions, Riccardo Morandi was enthusiastically taking up the subject of water tower design when the opportunity arose to erect two in an urban setting, the first in Leghorn and the other in Rome.

Water tower for the Leghorn aqueduct (project). In the first case, an elevated tank with a capacity of 44,000 gal., with its base 164ft., above ground level, was required to stand in the gardens between the railway station and the town of Leghorn. Morandi wanted this work to be absolutely clear both as to form and function, its character deriving solely from the correct proportioning of the functional elements of the work, considered as the components of an architectural whole.

He therefore decided to enclose the tank itself and the necessary auxiliary volumes within a trellis-work of inclined uprights arranged so as to form a ridged hyperboloid surface, the basic parameter of which, chosen to conform to the requirements of the subject, could provide dimensions and rigidity sufficient to resist the vertical action of the very considerable load, and the horizontal action of wind and possible earth tremors. The two spaces, enclosed within the double roof and the double base, could have been used as upper control rooms from which the pipes for the inflow and outflow of water could have been controlled. This piping system would have run in ducts within the inclined concrete struts forming the hyperboloid frame.

In addition to the weight of the water, the domed base of the tank would carry the weight of the intermediate circular partition, the two roofs, and the flooring of the lower chamber; this chamber is reached by a helical staircase which is structurally independent of the frame. The base of the structure contains, in addition, a chamber which houses all the pumping machinery.

The drawings fully illustrate this structure without the need for further description. They clearly show the compactness of the composition and the richness of the plastic and spacial effects that the finished work would have created in the natural setting for which it was designed.

Piezometric reservoir for the EUR area, Rome (project). At Rome, on the other hand, the considerable mass of the reservoir (770,000 gal.), and the agricultural nature of the region, which lies above the city, led Morandi to design first of all the actual water tank, in the shape of a simple elongated parallelepiped. Then, to preserve intact the purity of its shape he solved the problem of its support with three tall parallel wall-columns, one of which simply acts as a support, and two which have the further function of containing the piezometer, the vertical pipes and the staircases—all elements which are open to view and form part of the architectural composition. With these simple linear and functional structures, Morandi has produced a work that is at once sincere, and equally free from mannerisms and from traditional pre-conceptions. He has given the structure a form and a volume that can be clearly appreciated even from the furthest parts of the city.

The essentials of the composition—parallelepiped and wall-columns—must, however, stand on their own and be absolutely independent in relation to other forms and volumes of differing dimensions, including the control room and the underground reservoir; hence, the necessity for the vertical structure to spring directly from the ground, and at a suitable distance from the other buildings in the scheme.

The strict formal and volumetric composition of the tower led logically to the grouping of the ground-level structures in two masses only, and so avoiding 'bittiness' in the composition. In fact the whole value of the scheme resides in this unusual care for balanced layout and proportions.

A brief glance at the structures planned will suffice to complete the description of the project. The water tower was not intended as a group of related structures, but as a single cellular parallelepiped cantilevered over two supports, designed to contain the mass of water and resting, on the one hand, on a system of two vertical walls more than 130 ft. high, 36 ft. wide and varying in thickness from 31 in. to 43 in. (known as the piezometric tower) and, on the other hand, on a single wall similar to the preceding ones, which, as said above, acts solely as a support.

The stability of this structure against horizontal forces rests on the rigidity against bending of the 'piezometric' tower, which is obtained by making the two wall-columns act together transversely in the upper part of the tower with the enclosing wall of the piezometric tank for a height of 46 ft., and in the remainder of the tower with the curved beams of the staircase and the supporting framework of the piping. The low buildings which house the machinery and the control plant would have been roofed with solid, reinforced concrete slabs carried on multi-span frames. Light enters through large opening which would have given the water-works technicians a complete view of the piezometric tower.

The reinforced concrete structure would have been exposed, and the concrete cast in steel formwork with joints forming a restrained geometric pattern. In the central area of the large hall the control panel room and the transformer cabin would have been entirely enclosed in glass.

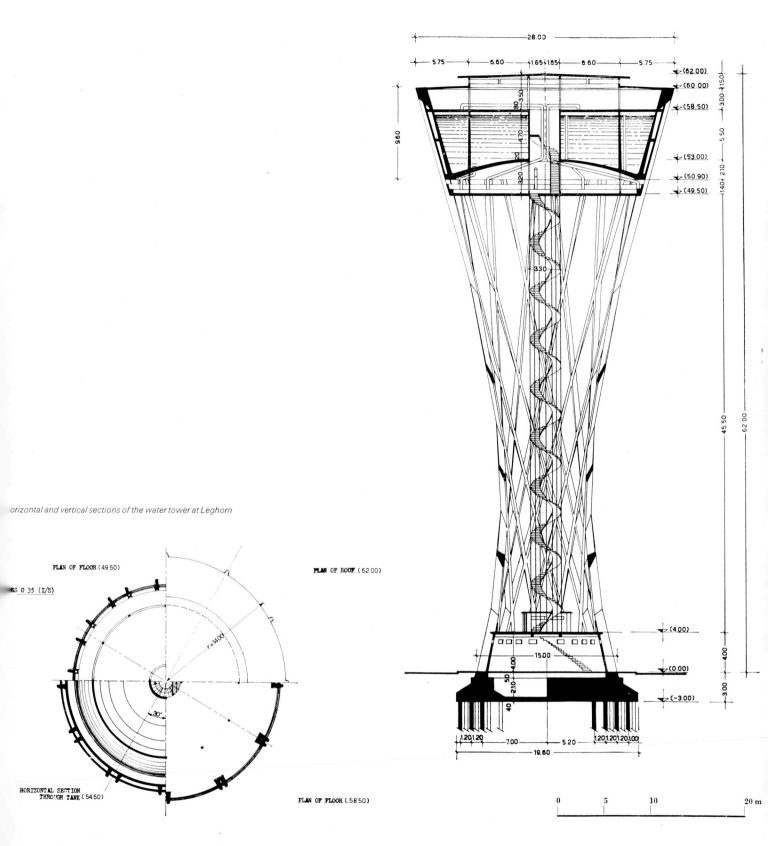

orizontal and vertical sections of the water tower at Leghorn

PLAN OF FLOOR (49.50)

PLAN OF ROOF (62.00)

6S 0 35 (I/S)

r = 14.00

30°

HORIZONTAL SECTION
THROUGH TANK (54.50)

PLAN OF FLOOR (58.50)

0   5   10   20 m

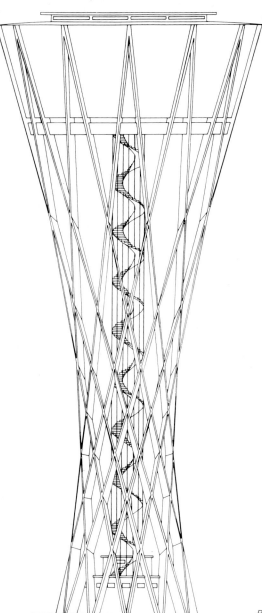

Perspective of the Leghorn water tower

Opposite: model of the water tower at Rome, seen from above, and plans of the scher

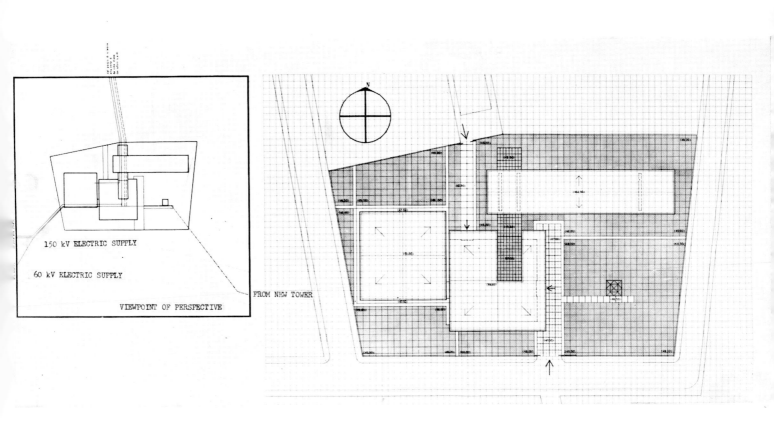

150 kV ELECTRIC SUPPLY

60 kV ELECTRIC SUPPLY

FROM NEW TOWER

VIEWPOINT OF PERSPECTIVE

203

staffe semplici (doppie)/single (double) stirrups : sagomati/shape

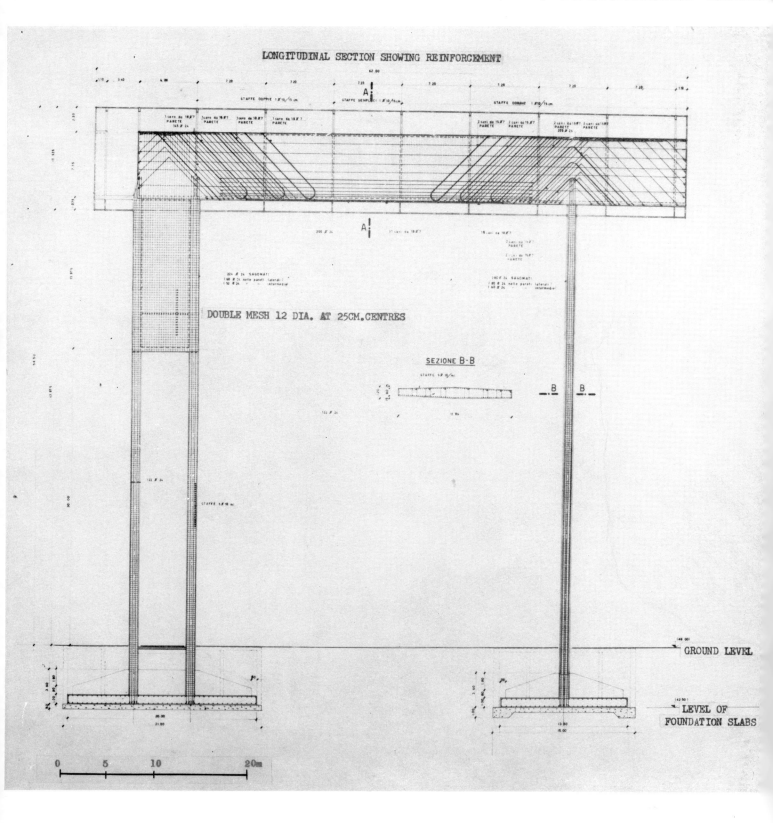

LONGITUDINAL SECTION SHOWING REINFORCEMENT

DOUBLE MESH 12 DIA. AT 25CM.CENTRES

SEZIONE B-B

GROUND LEVEL

LEVEL OF
FOUNDATION SLABS

0   5   10   20m

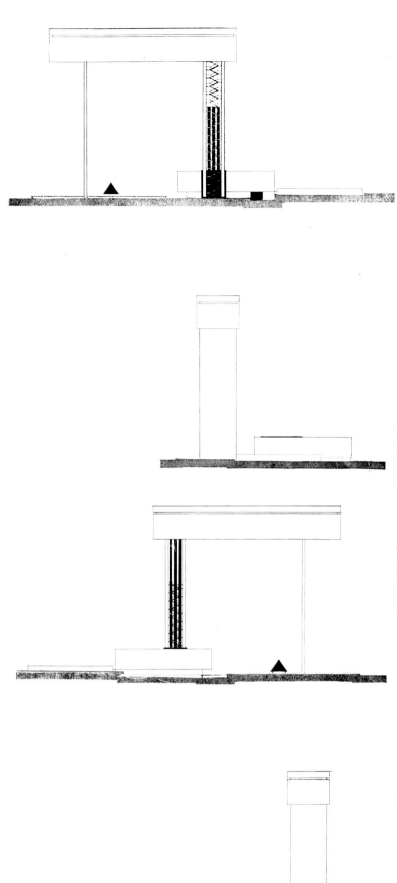

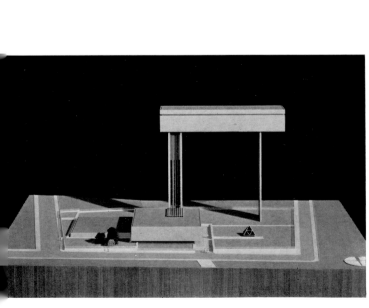

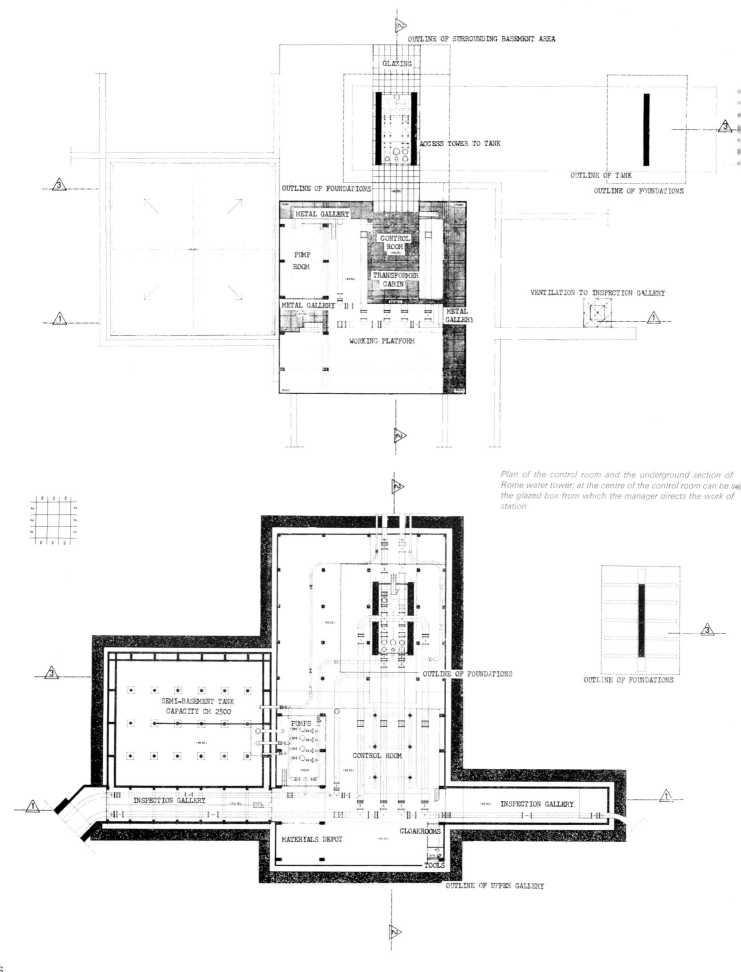

OUTLINE OF SURROUNDING BASEMENT AREA

GLAZING

ACCESS TOWER TO TANK

OUTLINE OF FOUNDATIONS

OUTLINE OF TANK

OUTLINE OF FOUNDATIONS

METAL GALLERY

PUMP ROOM

CONTROL ROOM

TRANSFORMER CABIN

METAL GALLERY

METAL GALLERY

WORKING PLATFORM

VENTILATION TO INSPECTION GALLERY

Plan of the control room and the underground section of Rome water tower; at the centre of the control room can be seen the glazed box from which the manager directs the work of station

OUTLINE OF FOUNDATIONS

OUTLINE OF FOUNDATIONS

SEMI-BASEMENT TANK CAPACITY CM 2500

PUMPS

CONTROL ROOM

INSPECTION GALLERY

INSPECTION GALLERY

MATERIALS DEPOT

CLOAKROOMS

TOOLS

OUTLINE OF UPPER GALLERY

206

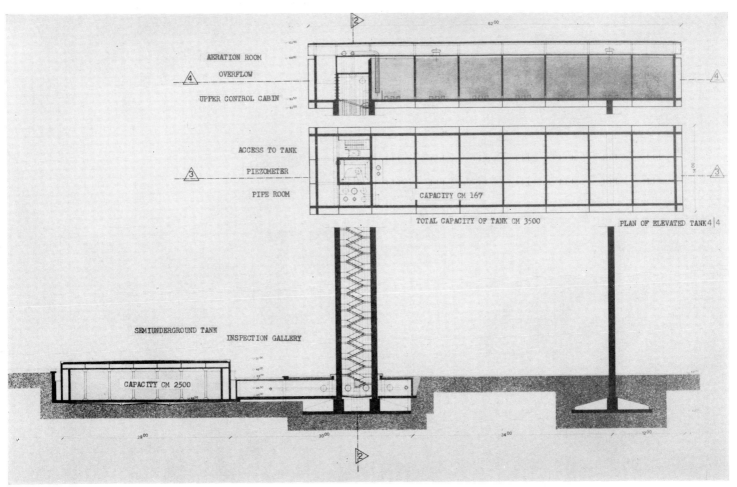

AERATION ROOM
OVERFLOW
UPPER CONTROL CABIN

ACCESS TO TANK
PIEZOMETER
PIPE ROOM

CAPACITY CM 167
TOTAL CAPACITY OF TANK CM 3500
PLAN OF ELEVATED TANK 4|4

SEMIUNDERGROUND TANK
INSPECTION GALLERY
CAPACITY CM 2500

Vertical section through the structure

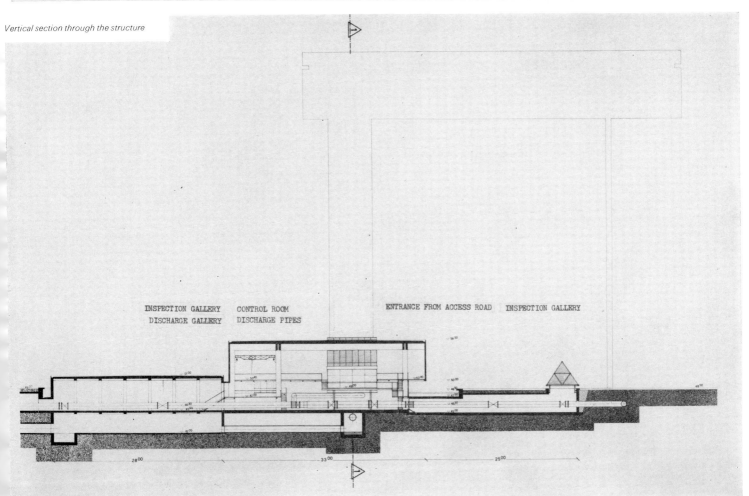

INSPECTION GALLERY   CONTROL ROOM
DISCHARGE GALLERY   DISCHARGE PIPES

ENTRANCE FROM ACCESS ROAD   INSPECTION GALLERY

208

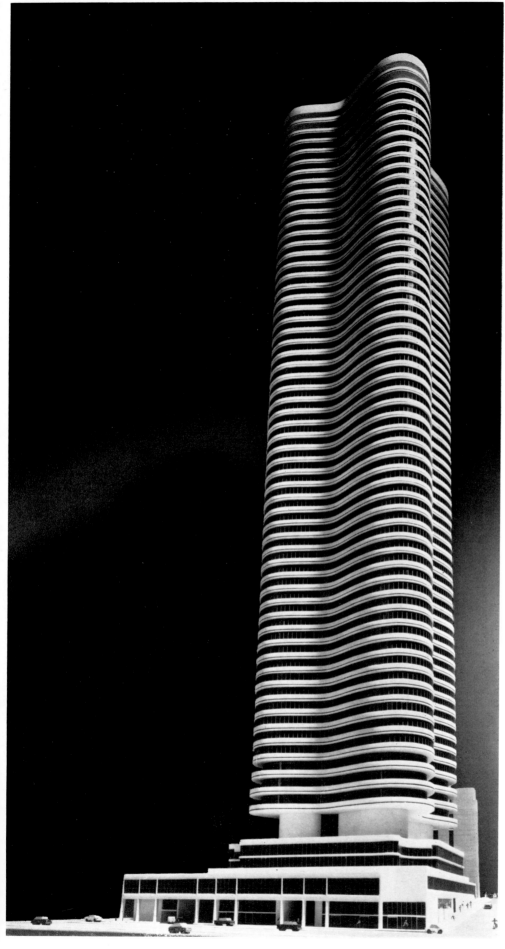

view of the model of the Peugeot building

Peugeot building at Buenos Aires, Argentina (project)

The project for this skyscraper, the only one ever designed by Riccardo Morandi, was drawn up in 1962, in connection with an international competition initiated by the Peugeot company for a large office building to be erected in Buenos Aires between Esmeralda Street and Libertador Avenue.

Both in form and in structure the building is very different from any other building of the type to have been erected in the more important American cities: it is, indeed, in complete contrast with anything that has been or is being done in North America in this field.

Both its form and its structure were, in fact, adopted by Morandi for visual and constructional reasons that were much more than secondary: on the one hand, to break with the tradition that could still visualize for this type of building nothing but the 'upright parallelepiped', and in this way to give a 'Latin' expression to certain constructional concepts, and, on the other hand, to experiment with highly efficient structural and constructional methods which were still new in the practical field, even if they had long been known in theory.

Moreover, the fact that the structure was planned for a commercial undertaking and, therefore, had an important promotional function, made it still more desirable to leave well-worn paths and go over to a freer expression of architectonic and structural values.

The main loadbearing structure of the building's most characteristic part, the tower—designed on a free plan and thus unforced in its application—consists of continuous vertical loadbearing slabs in reinforced concrete, of limited thickness and curved so as to provide the maximum rigidity against wind action and bending stresses induced by the horizontal elements. These are actually cantilevered beyond this central core and they also form a continuous prestressed concrete structure, to which the external curtain walling of glass and aluminium is fixed.

The building, designed for a total height of 794 ft., includes a base portion, partly underground, to contain garages, a commercial centre, a social and cultural centre, restaurant and bank, and the tall tower, occupied by the offices of the company and all the auxiliary services, which is served by fourteen lifts.

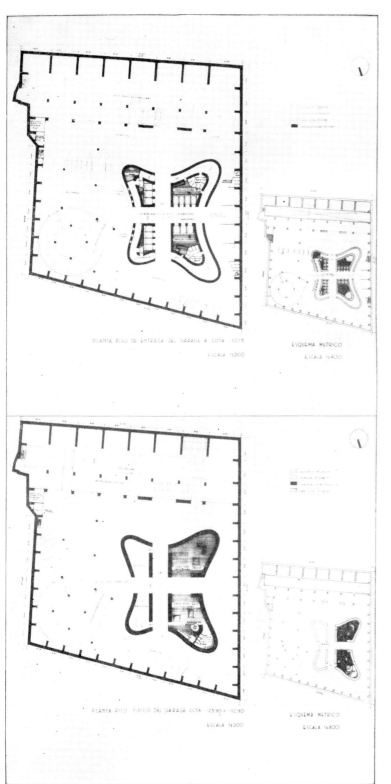

PLANTA PISO DE ENTREGA DEL GARAGE A COTA -10.15
ESCALA 1:200

ESQUEMA METRICO
ESCALA 1:400

PLANTA PISO TIPICO DEL GARAGE COTA -13.90 +-12.90
ESCALA 1:200

ESQUEMA METRICO
ESCALA 1:400

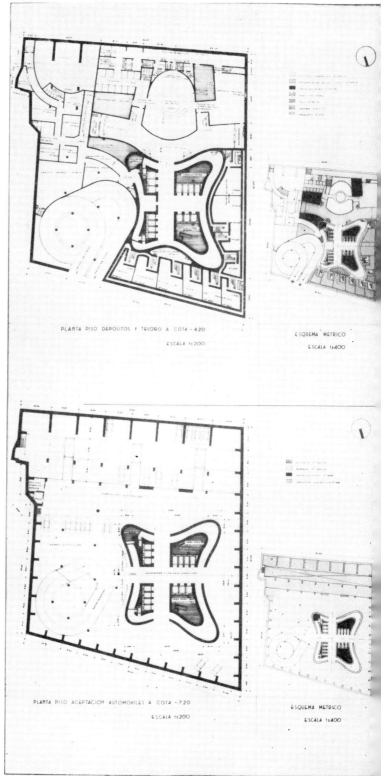

PLANTA PISO DEPOSITOS Y TESORO A COTA -4.20
ESCALA 1:200

ESQUEMA METRICO
ESCALA 1:400

PLANTA PISO ACEPTACION AUTOMOVILES A COTA -7.20
ESCALA 1:200

ESQUEMA METRICO
ESCALA 1:400

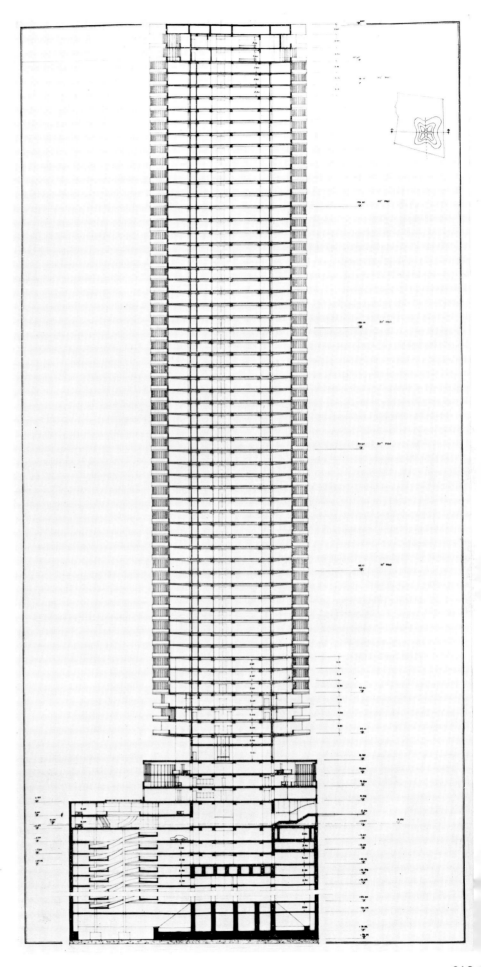

left: plan of various basement floors
right: vertical section (original drawing)

213

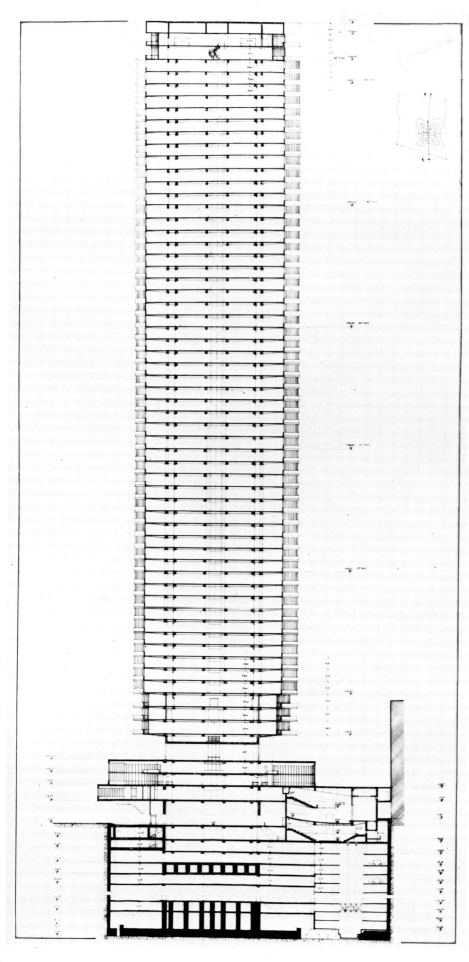

left: vertical section
right: plans of basement and of the office tower (original drawing.

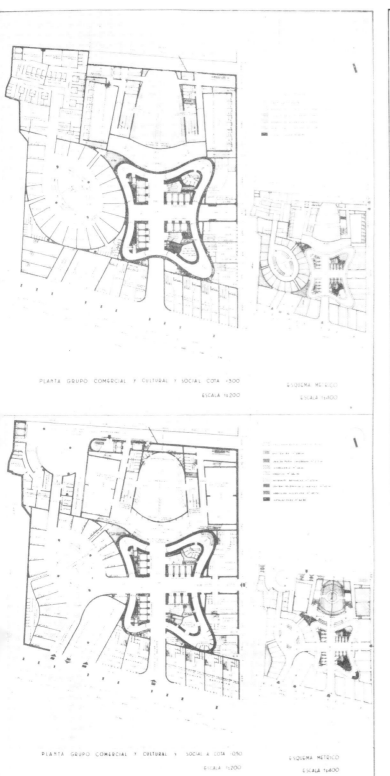

PLANTA GRUPO COMERCIAL Y CULTURAL Y SOCIAL COTA -3.00

ESCALA 1:200

ESQUEMA METRICO

ESCALA 1:400

PLANTA GRUPO COMERCIAL Y CULTURAL Y SOCIAL A COTA -0.50

ESCALA 1:200

ESQUEMA METRICO

ESCALA 1:400

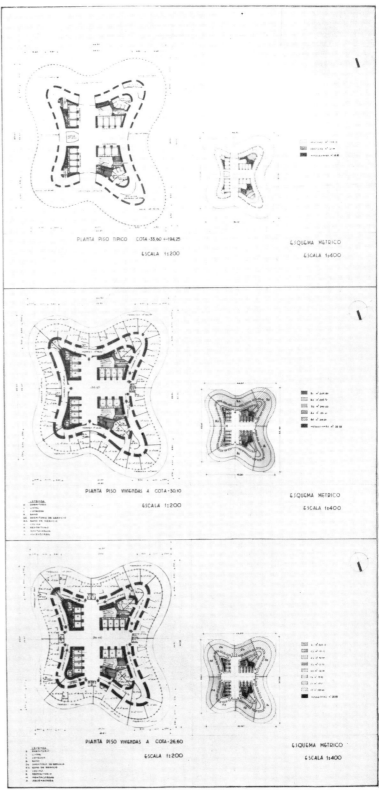

PLANTA PISO TIPICO COTA -33.60 +194.25

ESCALA 1:200

ESQUEMA METRICO

ESCALA 1:400

PLANTA PISO VIVIENDAS A COTA -30.10

ESCALA 1:200

ESQUEMA METRICO

ESCALA 1:400

PLANTA PISO VIVIENDAS A COTA -26.60

ESCALA 1:200

ESQUEMA METRICO

ESCALA 1:400

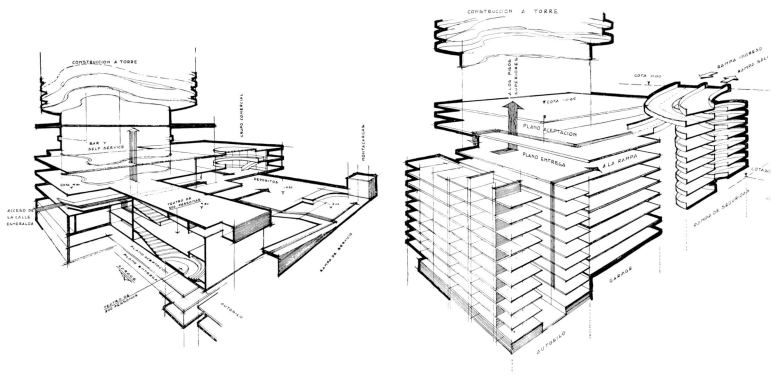

working diagram of the basement and underground garage (original drawings)

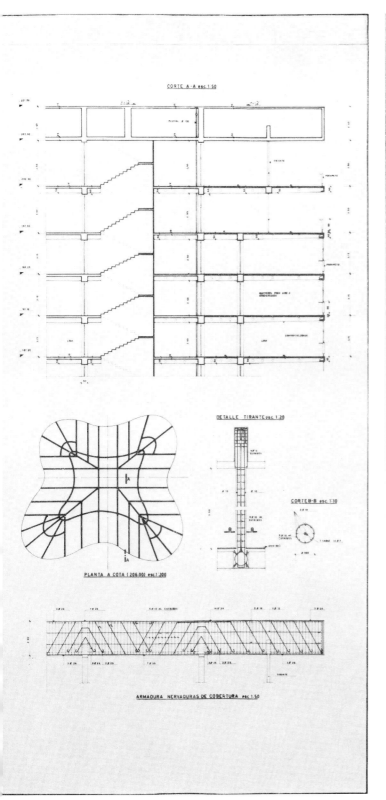

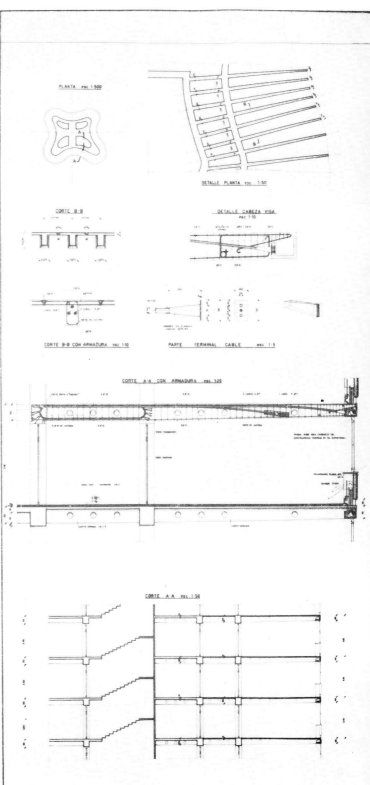

BIOGRAPHICAL NOTES AND BIBLIOGRAPHY

iccardo Morandi was born in Rome in 1902. He completed his studies there, securing his degree in 1927 at the Scuola di Applicazione per Ingegneri.

rom 1928 to 1931 he worked in Calabria on projects of structures in reinforced concrete for the new churches in the earthquake zones. After 1931 he made his headquarters in Rome where he still has his studio, and worked on projects for various parts of Italy and overseas.

rom 1936 he turned more and more towards profound studies in pre-stressed reinforced concrete, for which he has patents for more than one system bearing his name.

1958 he was a visiting professor in the technique on construction, and in 1959 he accepted the teaching of form and structure in bridges at the Facoltà di Architettura in the University of Florence. Recently he was awarded an honourable mention at the Biennale of Sao Paulo in Brazil for his work in the field of architecture. In 1963 the Associazione Italiana Tecnico Economica del Cemento awards were given to R. Morandi and R. L. Nervi.

is immense activity can be gauged from his archives which hold over 30,000 of his designs and projects, most of which have been executed.

He has written and published articles for many periodicals in Italy and overseas, illustrating his major works and technical methods and innovations used by him. A list is given here :

Su un tipo di balconata per sale da spettacoli, INDUSTRIA ITALIANA DEL CEMENTO, 1940 No. 12.

Contributo alla determinazione di un criterio di calcolo per strutture poste immediatamente al di sopra di una palificata, GIORNALE DEL GENIO CIVILE, April 1941.

Il nuovo ponte di S. Nicolo a Firenze, GIORNALE DEL GENIO CIVILE, 1949 No. 12.

Cinematografo Alcyone a Roma, DOCUMENTI DI ARCHITETTURA E INDUSTRIA EDILIZIA, 1950 No. 2.

Dispositivo per la realizzazione di strutture in cemento armato precompresso, GIORNALE DEL GENIO CIVILE, 1950 No. 3.

Coperture industriali a estradosso piano in calcestruzzo precompresso, INDUSTRIA ITALIANA DEL CEMENTO, September 1950.

Sur la réalisation d'ouvrages en béton précontrainte, ASSOCIATION SCIENTI-FIQUE DE LA PRÉCONTRAINTE, October 1950; and LA RICERCA SCIENTIFICA, 1951 No. 2.

Il nuovo ponte di calcestruzzo precompresso sul fiume Elsa a Canneto, GIORNALE DEL GENIO CIVILE, 1950 No. 12.

Due ponti in calcestruzzo precompresso, L'INGEGNERE, June 1951.

Serbatoio idrico a Pozzuoli, DOCUMENTI DI ARCHITETTURA E INDUSTRIA EDILIZIA, 1952 No. 12.

Una nuova grande coperture in calcestruzzo precompresso costruita in Roma, INDUSTRIA ITALIANA DEL CEMENTO, February 1952.

La ricostruzione del ponte del Grillo sul Tevere e del ponte di Castelfranco di Sotto sull'Arno, INDUSTRIA ITALIANA DEL CEMENTO, September 1952.

Sulla lettura diretta delle cadute di tensione per fluage in strutture di calcestruzzo precompresso, GIORNALE DEL GENIO CIVILE, 1953 No. 3.

Il ponte Giunture sul Liri in calcestruzzo precompresso, INDUSTRIA ITALIANA DEL CEMENTO, 1954 No. 2.

Una passarella costruita a Vagli di Sotto in Garfagnana, GIORNALE DEL GENIO CIVILE, 1954 No. 4.

New Storms River Bridge will be highest in Union, SHELL IN INDUSTRY, 1954 No. 8.

Ponte Nueva Republica a Caracas, DOCUMENTI DI ARCHITETTURA E INDUSTRIA EDILIZIA, 1955 No. 21.

Progress of the Storms River bridge, SHELL IN INDUSTRY, 1955 No. 11.

Advantages of Prestressed with particular reference to Statically Indeterminate Structures, JOURNAL OF THE INSTITUTE OF ENGINEERS (India), 1955 No. 7.

Un esempio di contemporanea adozione di ritrovi tecnici moderni per grandi edifici industriali, INDUSTRIA ITALIANA DEL CEMENTO, September 1955.

Le torri di ammarraggio per l'elettrodotto che attraversa lo stretto di Messina, GIORNALE DEL GENIO CIVILE, 1955 No. 10.

La pasarela de Vagli de Soto, INFORMES DE LA CONSTRUCCION, 1955 No. 75.

Un applicazione della precompressione nel campo delle grandi coperture industriali, L'ARCHITETTURA, 1955 No. 4.

Convenienza della Precompressione con speciale riguardo ai sistem iiperstatici, GIORNALE DEL GENIO CIVILE, 1956.

Il rafforzamento dell'ala dell'Arena di Verona mediante la precompressione, INDUSTRIA ITALIANA DEL CEMENTO, February 1956.

Ponte in precompresso sull'Autostrada Ligure, STRADE E TRAFFICO, 1956 No. 26.

Porticos pretensados para una nave industrial, INFORMES DE LA CONSTRUCCION, 1956 No. 11–12.

Il ponte sullo Storms River della Strada Nazionale Port Elizabeth—Cape Town, L'INGEGNERE, 1956 No. 8.

Puento algerado sobre el rio Storms, INFORMES DE LA CONSTRUCCION, 1957 No. 89.

Modern Conceptions in the Planning of Bridges in Reinforced Concrete and in Prestressed Concrete, ROADS AND ROAD CONSTRUCTION, 1957 No. 412.

Una grande intelaiatura in precompresso, L'ARCHITETTURA, 1957 No. 21.

Sulle condizioni di sicurezza nel tempo per tiranti pretesi disposti allo scopo di produrre distorsioni volute all'estremità di una trave, GIORNALE DEL GENIO CIVILE, 1957 No. 9.

Cine teatro Maestoso in Roma, INFORMES DE LA CONSTRUCCION, 1957 No. 94.

Sulla distrubuzione delle tensioni lungo cavi scorrevoli per strutture precompresse, INGEGNERE, 1957 No. 10.

Fabbricato in Roma per cinema-teatro ed abitazioni in Via Appia Nuova, INGEGNERI E ARCHITETTI, 1957 No. 11.

Ponte sul Lago di Maracaibo in Venezuela, L'ARCHITETTURA, 1957 No. 25.

Puenta Nueva Republica a Caracas, INFORMES DE LA CONSTRUCCION, 1957 No. 96.

Alcune recenti realizzazioni di strutture in calcestruzzo armato e in calcestruzzo precompresso, INGEGNERI E ARCHITETTI, 1953 No. 12.

Centro experimental a Roma, INFORMES DE LA CONSTRUCCION, 1960 No. 120.

Considerazioni sull'evoluzione dell'arte del costruire dei tempi nostri, TECNICA E UOMO, December 1960.

Qualche considerazione sull'attuale evoluzione dell'arte del costruire, L'INGEGNERI, 1961 No. 4.

Il progetto per il salvataggio dei templi di Abu Simbel, INCONTRI MEDITERRANEI, 1961 No. 2.

Salon del Automovil, INFORMES DE LA CONSTRUCCION, 1961 No. 129.

The Bridge spanning Lake Maracaibo, JOURNAL OF THE PRESTRESSED CONCRETE INSTITUTE, 1961 vol. 6, No. 2.

L'arco per il viadotto della Fiumerella presso Cantazaro, INDUSTRIA ITALIANA DEL CEMENTO, 1961 No. 7.

Die Strassenbrucke Nueva Republica in Caracas, DIE BAUTECHNIK, 196 No. 8.

Il ponte a Sulmona sul torrente Vella, L'INDUSTRIA ITALIANA DEL CEMENTO, 1962 No. 11.

Engineering and Architecture, JOURNAL OF THE ROYAL SOCIETY OF ARTS London 1962.

Moderni criteri di impostazione del progetto per il ponte stradale di medie e grand luci, XI CONVEGNO INTERNAZIONALE DELLE COMUNICAZIONI (Istituto Internazionale delle Comunicazioni, 1963).

L'incontro creativo fra ingegnere e architetto, ELSINORE, 1963.

Considerazioni sulla patologia del calcestruzzo armato, L'INDUSTRIA ITALIANA DEL CEMENTO, 1963.

Problèmes posès par la création de grands ponts et viaducs en béton, L'ARCHITECTURE D'AUJOURD'HUI, 1963.

La questione universitaria, ELSINORE, 1964.

Tied Bridges in Prestressed Concrete, CIVIL ENGINEERING, 1964.

Le nuove aviorimesse dell'Aeroporto di Roma-Fiumicino, L'INDUSTRIA ITALIANA DEL CEMENTO, 1964.

Sulle condizioni di sicurezza di esercizio di tiranti sottoposto a carichi variabi IL CEMENTO.

     *   *   *   *

In addition to various pamphlets illustrating his major works, R. Morandi ha also published *Forma e Struttura dei ponti* (University of Florence, 1959) which are summarised the lectures given by him at the Facoltà di Architettura the University of Florence, and *Strutture di calcestruzzo armato e di calcestruzz precompresso* (DEDALO, Rome 1954) in which are illustrated the most signi ficant works from his studio.

During the last few years R. Morandi has been invited to speak on his activitie and his research at many conferences at Societies and Associations in Europ and America:

April 1952 at Caracas on the execution of works in precompressed concrete 1955 at Amsterdam at the II Congress of the Fédération Internazionale de Précontrainte; February 1956 at Zurich at the Association Ponts et Chaussets 1956 at Naples at the Circolo Americano della N.A.T.O.: March 1957 London at the British Concrete Association; October 1957 at Venice at th V Seminario Internazionale di Architettura; November 1957 in Rome at th Consiglio Nazionale delle Ricerche where he spoke on recent works in r inforced concrete and prestressed concrete; 1959 in Turin at the Societ degli Ingegneri e Architetti on the same subjects; July 1960 in New York o the bridge over Lake Maracaibo; 1961 in Rome at the Accademia Naziona di S. Luca on the work on the Abu Simbel temples; 1961 in Rome at th Unione Romana Ingegneri e Architetti on prestressed reinforced concre and its uses in bridges; November 1961 in Edinburgh on reinforced concre and prestressed concrete structures; January 1962 in London at the Roy Society of Arts on engineering and architecture; February 1962 in Roma the Consiglio Nazionale delle Ricerche on the Lake Maracaibo bridge.

The following lists the principal publications on the works of R. Morandi:

Ponte di S. Nicolo sull'Arno a Firenze, DOCUMENTI DI ARCHITETTURA INDUSTRIA EDILIZIA, 1950 No. 2.

Puente en concrete precomprimido sobre el rio Tuy, by Leonardo Orteg REVISTA DEL COLEGIO DE INGENIEROS DE VENEZUELA, 1952 No. 19

Das Astoria Theater in Rom, by Luigi Lenzi, BAUWELT, 1953 No. 18.

Tomaso Kaserne in Rom, BETON UND STAHLBETONBAU, 1953 No. 6.

En Italiensk Betongkonstruktor, by Sten Gedda, BYGGMASTAREN, 195 No. 12.

Ponti sullo Storms River, sul Gornalunga, sul Mollarino, sul canale navigabile Fiumicino, torri di ammarraggio sullo stretto di Messina, stabilimento Castellaccio, centrale di Civitavecchia e centrale di Fiumicino, in U. Mante Cinquant'anni di lavoro, 1954.

Ponti in Sicilia, torri di ammarraggio sullo stretto di Messina, stabilimenti Castellaccio e di Colleferro, in Ferrocemento—Strutture in calcestruzzo pr compresso, Manzione, 1955.

n article on the work of R. Morandi in S. Africa in *South African Prestressed Concrete Development Group*, Johannesburg, November 1955.

centro studi della B.P.D. a Colleferro, by M. Rutelli, L'ARCHITETTURA, 1955, No. 4.

ubierta para una instalacion de carga y moliende de carbon, INFORMES DE LA CONSTRUCCION, 1956, No. 77.

Deposito elevado en Bagnoli, INFORMES DE LA CONSTRUCCION, 1956 No. 78.

Unique Road Bridge for Port Elizabeth, S. Africa, ACROW REVIEW, 1956 Vol. 2 No. 16.

wo prestressed Concrete Bridges with Hollow Girders of precast Vacuum-treated elements, by F. Piccinini and R. Morandi, JOURNAL OF THE AMERICAN CONCRETE INSTITUTE, 1956 No. 7.

wee bruggen in Sicilie, Silo van woorgespannen beton. Een brug over de Annea rivier. De contragewichttorens van het elektroduct over de Straat van Messina. Utiliteisgebouw in Castellaccio, POLYTECHNISCH TYDSCHRIFT, 1956 No. 15–16.

Constructies in gewapend beton en in vorgespannen beton, by P. Haas. A review of one of Morandi's books, CEMENT, 1956 No. 2–24.

Eisenbetonbrucken von Prof. R. Morandi, by H. Hofacker, SCHWEIZERISCHE BAUZEITUNG, 1957 No. 10.

Puente sobre el Maracaibo, INFORMES DE LA CONSTRUCCION, 1957 No. 91.

The Italian 'Morandi' system of prestressing, by A. Carbone, THE INDIAN CONCRETE JOURNAL, 1957 Vol. 31, No. 7.

Pont de Lupara sur l'Autoroute Genes-Savone; Ponts précontraints en Sicilie (Italie); Pont San Nicola près de Benevento (Italie); The Storms River bridge over the trunk road from Port Elizabeth to Cape Town (South Africa); Viaduc Nueva Republica à Caracas (Venezuela), BULLETIN DE L'ASSOCIATION INTERNATIONALE DES PONTS ET CHARPENTES, 1957 No. 16.

Recenti sviluppi degli studi e delle applicazioni del cemento armato precompresso in Italia, TECNICA MODERNA APPLICATA ALLA INGEGNERIA CIVILE, 1957 No. 3–4.

a centrale di Civitavecchia, Coppitelli 1954.

impianto termoelettrico di Fiumicino; l'impianto termoelettrico di Civitavecchia l'impianto termoelettrico di Santa Barbara, SOCIETÁ ROMANA DI ELLETRICITÁ, Ist. Graf. Bertieri, Milano 1958.

éton précontrainte, by Guyon (Editions Eyrolles) Paris 1958

he cinema-teatro Maestoso in Rome, by A. Carbone, INDIAN CONCRETE JOURNAL, November 1958.

ntwicklungstendenzen im Bau und Montage von Massivbrucken, by Hermann Bay, BETON HERTELLUNG VERWENDUNG, 1959 No. 5.

e prospettive future e le nuove fonti di energia (SENN); impianto di Santa Barbara della Soc. E. SELT-Valdarno e della S.R.E.; impianto di Civitavecchia della Soc. Termoel. Tirrena, INDUSTRIA ELETTRICA ITALIANA NEL 1958, Ist. Graf. Bertieri, Milano 1959.

as thermische Kraftwerk Santa Barbara in Italien, BROWN BOVERI MITTEILUNGEN, 1959 No. 3.

Die neue Flughafen von Rom; Die neue Stadio del Nuoto, by H. Hofacker, SCHWEIZERISCHE BAUZEITUNG, 1959 No. 27.

O novo pavilhao do Salao do Automovel da Exposiçao de Turim, ESTRUTURA, 1960 No. 25.

Il nuovo padiglione del Salone dell'Automobile a Torino—Esposizione, by R. Gabetti, L'ARCHITETTURA, 1960 No. 53.

Tecnicos Europeos de las obras del puente sobre el lago de Maracaibo EL INGENIERO, March 1960.

Maracaibobrucke in Venezuela by H. Hofacker, SCHWEIZERISCHE BAUZEITUNG, 1960 No. 42.

Padiglione dell'Automobile in Torino, DU, 1960 No. 237.

An underground hall in prestressed concrete, CONCRETE QUARTERLY, 1960 No. 47.

Cavalcavia della Via Olimpica su Corso Francia, UNIONE CEMENTI MARCHINO, 1961.

Puentes Italianos: San Nicolas en Benevento; Giunture sobre el Liri, by C. F. Casado, PUENTES DE HORMIGON ARMADO PRETENSADO, Dossat, Madrid 1961.

Il progetto italiano per salvare gli storici templi della Nubia, COSTRUTTORI ITALIANI NEL MONDO, 1961 No. 127.

Vous montre les réalisations récentes des meilleurs constructeurs Italiens, L'OEIL, 1961 No. 73.

Le giornate romane del precompresso, INDUSTRIA ITALIANA DEL CEMENTO, 1961 No. 3–4.

Pavillon des Automobilsalon in Torino-Esposizioni, by Ueli Roth, WERK, 1961 No. 4.

Wonders of the Ancient World now threatened with Complete Submersion: the two temples of Abu Simbel, THE ILLUSTRATED LONDON NEWS, 1961 No. 6358.

La monorataia Alweg a Torino by C. Bertolotti, INDUSTRIA ITALIANA DEL CEMENTO, 1961 No. 6.

Salone sotteraneo a Torino, L'ARCHITETTO, 1961 No. 7–8.

Four great pours, FORUM, 1961 No. 3.

Prestressed concrete crosses Lake Maracaibo, ENGINEERING NEWS RECORD, October 1961.

Il cavalcavia a Roma sul Corso Francia per la Via Olimpica, by Grauso, INDUSTRIA ITALIANA DEL CEMENTO, 1961 No. 11.

Aeropuerto international de Roma, INFORMES DE LA CONSTRICCION, 1961 No. 136.

Hall d'Exposition et garage à Turin, L'ARCHITECTURE D'AUJOURD'HUI, 1961 No. 99.

Via Olimpica, Quercia-Setta and Cisa viaducts; Maracaibo and Fiumarella bridges, L'ARCHITECTURE D'AUJOURD'HUI, November 1963.

Bridge over the Fiumarella, BULLETIN DE L'ASSOCIATION INTERNATIONALE DES PONTS ET CHARPENTES, 1963

Bridge on Lake Maracaibo, VOM BAU DER BRUCKE, 1963.

INDEX TO PRINCIPAL WORKS OF R. MORANDI

2

8   9

4

10

6

11

(The items in bold type refer to works illustrated in this book.)

1. Piccini garage, via delle Fornaci, Rome (1932–33). Builders: G. I. Magrini (One of the first important examples of a hyperstatic frame in reinforced concrete.)
2. Augustus cinema Corso Vittorio Emanuele, Rome (1933–34). Carried out in collaboration. Builders: Giovannetti.
3. Parish church at Colleferro, near Rome (1934–35). Builders: G. I. Magrini. (One of the first examples of reinforced concrete in natural finish.)
4. Giulio Cesare cinema, Viale G. Cesare, Rome (1934–36). Builders: Giovannetti. (One of the very first examples of a cinema balcony with balanced torsion.)
5. Colleferro cement works, near Rome (1935). Builders: Magrini.
6. S. Giorgio bridge, over the River Liri (1945–47). (Beams with counterweighted ends.) Builders: Bajocchini-Cinti-Rinversi.
7. S. Nicolo bridge, Florence (1945–48). Winning project in a national competition. Builders: Giovannetti. (Large single span with recessed vaulting, without bearing spandrels.)
8. Astoria cinema, Via Stoppani, Rome (1946–47). Builders: G. I. Magrini.
9. Bologna cinema, Rome (1947–48). Builders: de Rubeis.
10. Del Grillo bridge over the Tiber (1948–49). Builders: Bajocchini-Cinti-Rinversi.
11. Enlargement and adjustment to old Roman Valentino bridge over the River Calore (1948, project). (The work was to consist of a light structure in reinforced concrete supporting the old road independently of the existing mural structure.)

225

12

13

18

14

15

16

19

20

17

12. Alcyone cinema, Via Lago di Lesino, Rome (1949–50). In collaboration with architect Gia~ Gandolfi. Builders: Fraschetti.

13. Bridge over the Elsa torrent in Tuscany (1949–50). (The first bridge by R. Morandi in p~ stressed reinforced concrete.) Builders: Giovannetti.

14. Segni cement works, Scafa S. Valentino near Pescara (1949–51). Builders: Catola.

15. Enlargement of the S.R.E. central thermo-electric station, Rome (1949–50). Builde~ Giovannetti. (An interesting example of a staircase in reinforced concrete hung on iron ~ rods.)

16. Espero cinema, Via Nomentana, Rome (1950). Builders: Salce.

17. Mess for the G.C. di Tomaso barracks in Rome (1950–51). Builders: Giovannetti. (The first example of a large span in pre-stressed reinforced concrete using the 'Mora~ system'.)

18. C.I.F. works, Zaule near Trieste (1950–52). Builders: Federici.

19. Auditorium for the Accademia di Musica S. Cecilia, Rome (1950). Project which won th~ prize in the national competition (in collaboration with architects Cosma Carrara and Pie~ Maruffi.)

20. Floating bridge across Lake Paola, near Sabaudia (1950, project). This was to have a serie~ beams resting on separate floating caissons in reinforced concrete.

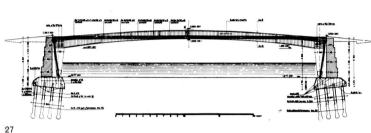

26

27

28

24

21. Eden cinema in Rome (1950–52).

22. Bridge over the River Tuy near Caracas in Venezuela (1950–51). Built by the Italo-Venezuelan 'Precomprimido C.A.' company which was founded in Latin America to exploit the pre-stressed concrete patents granted by R. Morandi. (One of the first pre-stressed reinforced concrete applications in South America.)

23. Nueva Republica bridge, Paguita-Caracas in Venezuela (1951–54). Built by the Precomprimido C.A. company. (Winning project in an international competition fostered by the Ministry of Public Works in Venezuela. (Page 25).

24. S.T.T. central thermo-electric power station in Civitavecchia (1951–52). Builders: Mantelli (page 107).

25. Bridge over the River Arrestra on the Genoa-Savona autostrada (1951–52). Builders: Drighetti-Masotti. (Arch of 100 metres.)

26. Delle Compere bridge, over the River Liri at Sora near Frosinone (1952–53). Builders: Bajocchini-Cinti-Rinversi.

27. XX Settembre bridge over the River Liri at Sora near Frosinone (1952–53). Builders: Bajocchini-Cinti-Rinversi.

28. Delle Giunture bridge over the River Liri (1952–53). Builders: Giovannetti. (Use of a typical 'Morandi frame' as main support to a bridge.)

29

30

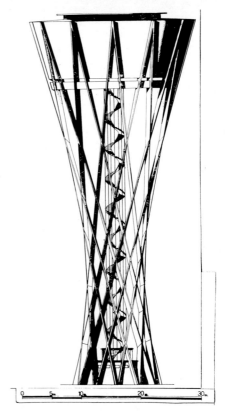

34

31

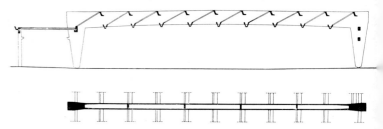

35

32   33

29. A.B.C.D. cement works at Ragusa in Sicily (1952–53).

30. Hangar at La Guaria near Caracas, Venezuela (1952, project).

31. Bridge over the Lupara torrent, at Arenzano near Genoa, for the Genoa-Savona autostrad (1952–53). Builders: Bajocchini-Cinti-Rinversi.

32. B.P.D. 'Tecnicum' at Colleferro near Rome (1953–54). Builders: Sebastiani.

33. Footbridge over the Lussia torrent at Vagli di Sotto, near Lucca (1953–54 Builders: Giovannetti. (Erected with pre-cast rotated semi arches constructe on land.) (Page 31.)

34. Water tower for the Leghorn aqueduct (1953, project). (Based on shaped trell work of inclined uprights.) (Page 199.)

35. Lazzi garage in Florence (1953–54). (Frame in pre-stressed reinforced concrete in th 'Morandi systems', with 35 metres span.) Builders: Giovannetti.

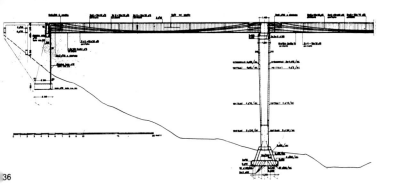

36

7

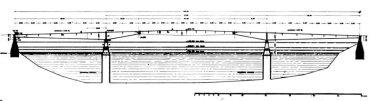

8

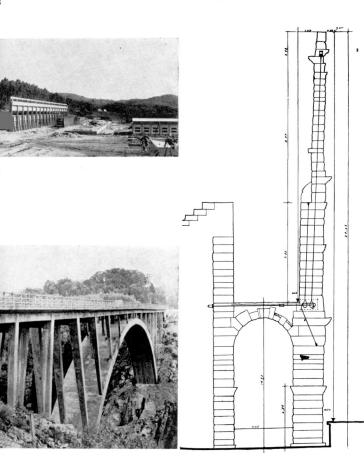

9

41

42

43   44

45

36. Bridge over the Tambura torrent at Vaglia di Sotto, near Lucca (1953–54). (Built with pre-stressed beams resting on high supports.) Builders : Giovannetti.
37. Bridge over the Agro and Fiumedinisi torrents in Sicily (1953–54). (Built in reinforced concrete with pre-fabricated hollow beams in pre-stressed concrete.) Builders : Ferrocemento.
38. Bridge over the River Adda at Lecco (1953–54).
39. S. Rita cement works near Sao Paulo, Brazil (1953–54).
40. **Bridge over the Storms River near Elizabethville in S. Africa (1953–54). Builders : Concor. (Winning project in an international competition sponsored by the national trunk roads authorities of S. Africa.) (Page 37.)**
41. Static reinforcement of a dangerous section of the Verona Arena (1953). Carried out by the Sovrintendenza alle Antichità delle Venezie. (Example of the use of pre-stressed elements in a supporting wall.) Builders : Else.
42. B.P.D. studio at Colleferro near Rome (1954). Builders : Ferrocemento.
43. Factory for synthetic and natural fibres, for the B.P.D. company at Castellaccio, near Rome (1954–55). Builders : Ferrocemento.
44. Metallurgical centre of B.P.D. at Colleferro, near Rome (1954). Builders : Ferrocemento.
45. Mooring tower for electric cables across the Straits of Messina, Sicily (1954–55). Builders Ferrocemento.

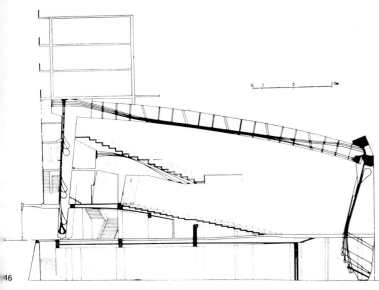

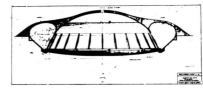

46 50 51

47

48

52

9

46. Maestoso cinema in Via Appia Nuova, Rome (1954–55). Builders: Ferrocemento. (The construction of the auditorium is built up with reinforced concrete frames with spans of 40 metres

47. The Amerigo Vespucci bridge over the Arno, Florence (1954–55). In collaboration with architects G. & P. Gori and F. Nerli. Builders: Giovannetti. (Page 101)

48. S. Nicola bridge at Benevento (1954–55). Builders: Bajocchini-Cinti-Rinversi.

49. Santa Barbara power station at S. Giovanni Valdarno, near Florence (1954–55) Builders: Giovannetti. (Page 115).

50. Underground reservoir for oil at Caracas, Venezuela (1955, project).

51. Segni cement works at Savignano (1955–58). Builders: Magrini.

52. Fiat works near Naples (1956–57). In collaboration with the construction department of the Fiat company. Builders: Decina-Giovannetti.

53

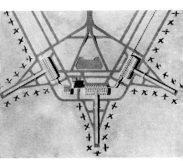

58

59

54

55

60

61

56

57

53. Metronio covered market with garage above, in Via Magna Grecia, Rome (1956–57). Builders: Sirte.

54. Bridge over the Sambro torrent for the Autostrada del Sole, near Bologna (1957–58). Builders: Sogene.

55. **Quercia-Setta viaduct on the Autostrada del Sole, near Bologna (1957–58). Builders: Sogene. (Page 87.)**

56. **Bridge over Lake Maracaibo, Venezuela (1957–62). Builders: Consorcio Puente Maracaibo. (Winning project in an international competition; all the projects submitted to the jury, excepting that of Morandi, were for a bridge in iron instead of reinforced concrete.) (Page 144.)**

57. Bridge giving access to the International Aerodrome at Rome, across the Fiumicino canal (1957–58). (Only part of Morandi's project was carried out.) Builders: Ferrocemento.

58–59. Terminal building for the International Aerodrome at Fiumicino near Rome (1957–60). In collaboration with Architect A. Zavitteri, and executed with the co-operation of the Architects V. Monaco and A. Luccichenti. Builders: Provera & Carrassi. (Winning project in an international competition.)

60. **Viaduct over the Fiumerella valley, near Catanzaro (1958–62). Builders: Sogene. (Page 43.)**

61. **A.B.C.D. works at Ragusa, Sicily (1958–59). (Page 123.)**

62

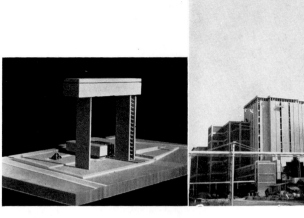

67   63

3

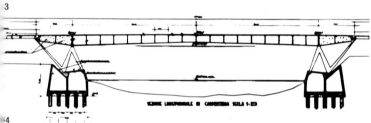

4

69

70

5

62. Underground car hall in the Valentino Park, Turin (1958–59). Builders: Sogene. (Page 53.)

63. Via Olimpico viaduct over Corso Francia, Rome (1958–59). Builders: Marino-Ciarlante. (Page 73.)

64. Bridge over the Tiber, at Tor di Quinto in Rome (1959, project).

65. Palace of Labour for the Italia '61 Exhibition, Turin (1959, project). In collaboration with architects R. Gabetti and A. Isola. (Page 67.)

66. S.E.N.N. nuclear power station at Garigliano (1959–62). Builders: Italstrade. (Page 131.)

67. Piezometric reservoir for the EUR area, Rome (1960, project). In collaboration with architects G. Boaga, B. Boni and M. Ingrami. (Page 200.)

68. SELT-Valdarno thermo-electric power station at Leghorn (1960–65). Builders: S.A.C.I.P. (Page 137.)

69. Olympic stadium for the Sports City, Teheran (1960, project awaiting implementation). In collaboration with architect A. Zavitteri. (Page 193.)

70. Bridge over the Vella at Sulmona (1960–62). Builders: Decina. (Page 80.)

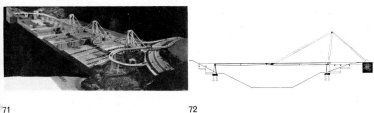

71

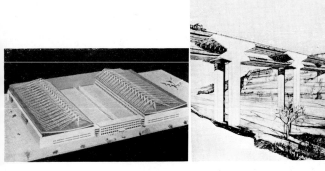

72

73 74

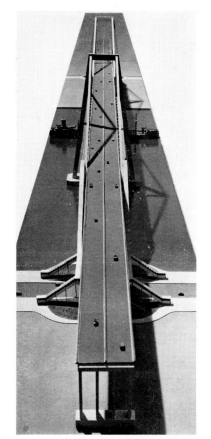

78

76

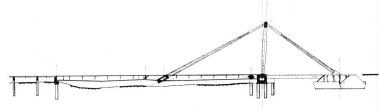

79

5 76

7

80

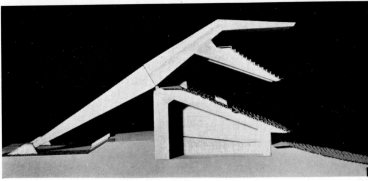

82

81

83

80. Bridge on the Columbia River, Canada (1963, under construction).
81. Overpass bridge on Via Cristoforo Colombo at Casal Palocco, Rome (1963). Builders: Soc. Generale Immobiliare.
82. Stadium in Munich (1964, project).
83. Latte Valley viaduct near Franco-Italian border (1965, project).

PHOTOGRAPHIC ACKNOWLEDGEMENTS

We are indebted to the following for the photographs:
Antoci, Ragusa, 222; Armone, Messina, 223; Barsotti, Firenze, 118, 136, 139; Carbone, Genova, 221; Cervi, Sora, 221; Consorcio Puente Maracaibo, Maracaibo, 142, 147, 148, 150–154, 157–165, 167, 225; d'Amico, Rome, 219; Doudney, Cape Town, 41; Eastern Province Herald, Cape Town 39, 223; Felici, Savignano, 224; Frattali, Anagni, 223; Germani Cisterna, Rome, 168, 170, 182, 192, 196, 197, 227; Gianni Pra, Rome, 4, 23, 30, 36, 49–52, 54, 57–59, 65, 72, 79, 82, 83, 85, 86, 89–94, 102, 103, 105, 106, 109–111, 113. 114, 117–120, 133–135, 167, 190, 191, 198, 203, 205, 209, 222–226; Ilario, Catanzaro, 42, 44, 46, 48; Lastrucci, S. Giovanni Valdano, 117, 118, 224; Locchi, Firenze, 140, 226; Lo Presti, Ragusa, 122, 125–129, 225; Moncalvo, Turin, 55, 56, 63; Morandi, Rome, 27, 29, 33, 34, 36, 64, 81, 95, 130, 219–225; Pesce, Rome, 219; Pittia Muggia, 220; Publifoto, Genova, 172, 173; Rastrelli, Firenze 121; Salvini, Firenze 219,220; Sciamanna Rome, 221; SELT, Valdarno, Firenze, 226; Universal, Turin, 60, 61; Vasari, Rome, 69, 71, 75–77, 171, 185, 188, 210, 219–223, 226, 227; Morandi archives, 38, 66, 88, 96, 104, 116, 123, 149, 152, 156,186, 194,195,201, 203–207 220–227.